Disney's

KiM POSSIBLE

SO NOT THE DRAMA

BADICAL!

Weekends at 6:30pm/5:30c

A Disney Channel Original Series

ZoogDisney.com

Disney CHANNEL

©Disney

Betty and Veronica in "The WELCOMING COMMITTEE"

LOOK AT THOSE TWO FRESHMAN GIRLS! DID YOU EVER SEE ANYONE SO SCARED IN YOUR LIFE?

MMPH! YES! I DID ONCE!

YOU AND ME ON *OUR* FIRST DAY IN HIGH SCHOOL!

OH, GOLLY! IS *THAT* EVER THE TRUTH!

AGNES, I'M SCARED TO DEATH!

ME TOO, SUSAN! I HOPE WE GET USED TO IT SOON!

1

LEARN TO DRAW
Betty

769 D

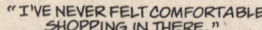

"I'VE NEVER FELT COMFORTABLE SHOPPING IN THERE."

GEE, I FEEL THE SALESPEOPLE ARE FOLLOWING ME WHEREVER I GO.

THAT'S WHY I DON'T CARE MUCH FOR BLOOMRITZ'S.

OH, YOU'RE BEING SILLY, BETTY. IT'S ALL IN YOUR MIND!

"WHENEVER I GO INTO BLOOMRITZ'S, I GET ROYAL TREATMENT ..."

GOOD DAY, MISS! MAY I HELP YOU?

I HOPE SO! I'M LOOKING FOR A NEW DRESS.

WHAT SIZE, MISS? WHAT COLOR? WHAT STYLE?

" IN FACT, THEY WAIT ON ME HAND AND FOOT!"

IT MAY INTEREST YOU TO KNOW, WE'RE HAVING A SALE ON GLOVES TODAY!

WILL YOU BE NEEDING SHOES TO GO WITH THAT DRESS?

③

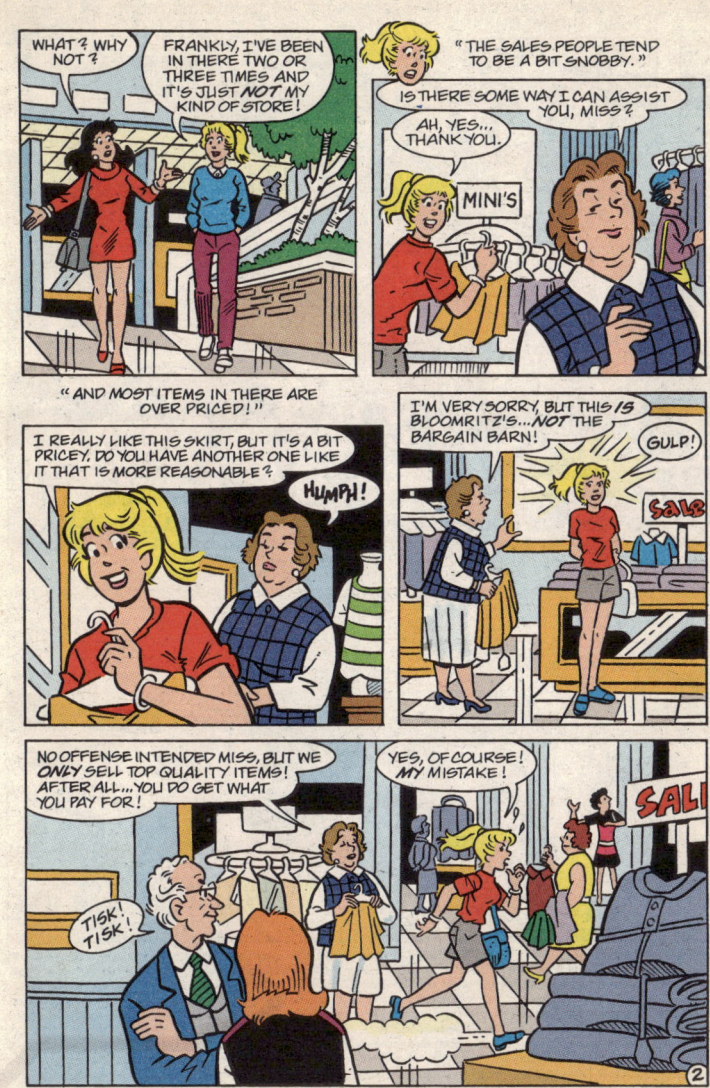

DON'T YOU JUST LOVE SHOPPING AT THE SOUTH SIDE MEGA-MALL?

TO TELL THE TRUTH, I DON'T SHOP HERE VERY OFTEN.

Betty & Veronica in Prized Patron!

SCRIPT: MIKE PELLOWSKI PENCILS: TIM KENNEDY INKS: RUDY LAPICK
COLORS: BARRY GROSSMAN LETTERS: VICKIE WILLIAMS
EDITORS: NELSON RIBEIRO & VICTOR GORELICK EDITOR-IN-CHIEF: RICHARD GOLDWATER

I ONLY AGREED TO COME TODAY TO PLEASE YOU!

WELL, I COME HERE MAINLY TO GO TO BLOOMRITZ'S DEPT. STORE!

THERE IT IS! COME! LET'S GO IN AND SHOP TIL WE DROP!

I'D RATHER NOT!

BETTY AND VERONICA DOUBLE DIGEST MAGAZINE (ISSN:10440321), No. 109, Nov., 2002. Published 9 times a year in Feb., Mar., Apr., May, July, Aug., Oct., Nov. and Dec. by Archie Comic Publications, Inc., 325 Fayette Avenue, Mamaroneck, New York 10543-2318. Richard H. Goldwater, President and Co-Publisher. Michael I. Silberkleit, Chairman and Co-Publisher. ARCHIE characters created by John L. Goldwater. The likenesses of the original Archie characters were created by Bob Montana. Single copies $3.29 in the U.S.; $3.99 in Canada. Subscription rate: U.S. $29.61 for 9 issues; $35.91 in Canada. All Canadian orders payable in U.S. funds. "Betty and Veronica Double Digest Magazine" and the individual characters'

LAST TERM WE WERE BIG SHOTS IN GRAMMAR SCHOOL, AND NOW WE'RE BACK DOWN AT THE BOTTOM AGAIN!

RIGHT!

SOMEONE FOR THE SOPHOMORES, JUNIORS AND SENIORS TO KICK AROUND!

KNOW WHAT THEY'VE GOT? THEY'VE GOT THE UPPERCLASSMAN WORRIES!

RIGHT!

THEY WERE PRETTY MEAN TO US IN OUR DAY!

OH, WOW! THE TRICKS THE GALS USED TO PULL ON US!

DON'T LOOK NOW, SUSAN, BUT THERE'S A COUPLE OF THEM WATCHING US NOW!

UH, OH!

I GUESS WE'RE IN FOR IT! I HOPE IT ISN'T ANYTHING TOO TERRIBLE!

ME TOO!

2

WHY DON'T WE DO SOMETHING NICE FOR THEM TO SHOW THEM THAT WE'RE NOT *ALL* MEAN AND NASTY?

THAT'S A WONDER-FUL IDEA!

WHY DON'T WE BUY THEM A NICE *LUNCH* AS A WELCOMING GESTURE?

IN OUR CAFETERIA? THAT'S NO GESTURE OF FRIENDSHIP!

OH, NO! NOT ONE OF MISS BEAZLY'S TIRED OLD LUNCHES!

SOME-THING FROM OUTSIDE!

A BUCKET OF THE COLONEL'S CHICKEN! THEY'LL *LOVE* IT!

AND SOME FRIES AND MALTS!

CHICKEN

YOO HOO! YOU FROSH!

FRONT AND CENTER!

ULP! THIS IS IT, AGNES! HERE IT COMES!

I WONDER WHAT MEANNESS THEY'VE DREAMED UP?

3

GIRLS, WELCOME TO RIVERDALE HIGH!

AS A GESTURE OF OUR FRIEND-SHIP WE'VE BOUGHT YOU A LOVELY LUNCH!

LOOK, AGNES! FRIED CHICKEN! ISN'T THAT WONDERFUL?

OH, THANK YOU! YOU MAKE US FEEL AT HOME!

NOW YOU RUN ALONG AND EAT THAT NICE LUNCH AND REMEMBER THAT YOU'RE AMONG FRIENDS!

FAT CHANCE! I'D RATHER STARVE!

I WONDER WHAT ROTTEN THING THEY'VE DONE TO IT?

SUSAN! I'VE GOT AN IDEA! THERE'S THAT BIG GUY THAT'S SUPPOSED TO LIKE EATING SO MUCH!

OOOH!

THEY TOLD YOU TO GIVE IT TO ME?

I THINK THEY LIKE YOU BUT THEY'RE TOO SHY TO MENTION IT!

④

The End

Betty and Veronica in "HEADS UP"

WHAT'S **WRONG** WITH MY HAIR?

SHEESH! HOW SHALL I TELL THEE? LET ME COUNT THE WAYS!

IT'S MOUSEY LOOKING, IT'S TIRED, IT'S COMMONPLACE---

ER--- I THINK THAT'S ENOUGH!

IT'S OUT OF STYLE, OUTDATED--- OUTMODED---

I **SAID**, THAT WAS ENOUGH!

I HAVE A NATURAL TALENT FOR HAIRSTYLING! WHY DON'T YOU LET ME GIVE IT A WHIRL?

OH, YES, YES, NANCY! BY ALL MEANS! BE MY GUEST!

WELL... LET'S GO!

MONDAY--

WOW! IS THAT YOU, BETTY?

I LIKE IT! I LIKE IT!

TUESDAY---

WAY TO GO, BETTY!

WHAT A PRETTY LITTLE PACKAGE!

WEDNESDAY--

HOW LONG IS THIS GOING TO GO ON?

IS THIS THE SAME GIRL I FELL IN LOVE WITH YESTERDAY?

BETTY, YOU'RE THE TALK OF THE TOWN!

MY! THAT BRINGS BACK FOND MEMORIES!

3

THURSDAY—

LOVE IT, BETTY! JUST LOVE IT!

I CAN'T DECIDE WHICH DAY I LIKE BEST!

FRIDAY—

HOW ABOUT A DATE EVERY NIGHT NEXT WEEK? IT'LL BE LIKE DATING FIVE GORGEOUS GIRLS!

ALL RIGHT! ALL RIGHT! WHAT'S GOING ON?

I THOUGHT YOU COULDN'T AFFORD A HAIRSTYLIST?

I CAN'T!?!

NANCY'S BEEN FIXING MY HAIR EVERYDAY!

HMPH! I THOUGHT THERE WAS SOMETHING AMATEUR ABOUT IT!

ANYBODY CAN FIX THICK, COMMON-TYPE HAIR!

MY HAIR IS MUCH TOO FINE AND ELEGANT FOR THAT SORT OF NONSENSE!

4

The End

ISP required. Ask your parents before going online.

In the dark of the night, the gang is gathered at Archie's house. They are patiently awaiting the arrival of Jughead, who is supposed to be bringing some delicious Tony's® Pizza. As he is approaching Archie's, a chill runs through Jughead's body. He turns around just in time to see a glimmering shape appear out of the darkness. Before he knows what is happening, Jughead is on the ground and the precious Tony's® Pizza is gone!

Help the gang figure out who stole the Tony's® Pizza by answering the Archie trivia questions and using all the circled letters to reveal the culprit. Good Luck!

. **What is Veronica's Fathers name?**

. **Where is the gang's most popular hangout?**

. **Who is Brigitte dating from Riverdale?**

. **What is the name of Betty's NEW love interest?**

. **What is Jughead's real name?**

. **What new character recently took a trip to New York to cover Fashion week as a teen reporter?**

Answers: 1. Hiram, 2. Pop's, 3. Dilton, 4. Adam, 5. Forsythe, 6. Ginger

WELL, GIRLS, WHAT SORT OF SUMMER DID YOU HAVE?

FRAUGHT WITH EXCITEMENT, I'D WAGER!

NOT ME! I JUST HUNG AROUND THE HOUSE! NOTHING UNUSUAL!

Betty and Veronica "THE HOMEBODY"

NOW *THAT'S* UNUSUAL IN ITSELF! VERONICA LODGE! THE GREAT WORLD TRAVELER, STAYED AT HOME!

UNBELIEVABLE!

ER-- RON! DON'T YOU THINK "HANGING AROUND THE HOUSE" CALLS FOR A BIT MORE *DETAIL?*

LIKE WHAT?

I KNOW HOME IS WHERE YOU HANG YOUR HAT,---BUT---

YOU KNOW I SELDOM WEAR HATS!

TELL US ABOUT THE FIRST WEEK IN *JULY!*

YAWN! SO WHAT'S TO TELL?

OUR BEACH SHACK IN HAWAII DOESN'T CHANGE MUCH FROM YEAR TO YEAR!

-YOU SEE ONE MEGABODIED BEACH BOY, YOU'VE SEEN THEM ALL!

IT WAS BORING, SO WE TOOK OFF FOR OUR HOUSE IN THE SOUTH OF FRANCE!

"HANGING AROUND THE HOUSE!"

TSK, TSK!

NO EXCITEMENT THERE, EITHER! I ALMOST *MISSED* SCHOOL!

2

— ON TO OUR SWISS CHALET TO GET OUT OF THE DOLDRUMS!

THOSE DOLDRUMS IN THE SUMMER ARE VERY NASTY!

HOW TRUE!

AT LEAST WE GOT IN A BIT OF SKIING FOR A CHANGE OF PACE!

MY! HOW AWFUL... TO BE *HOUSE* BOUND LIKE THAT!

INDEED!

— SO TRAGIC TO BE BORED ALL OVER THE *WORLD!*

ALL IT TAKES IS A BILLION OR SO!

— AND DID *YOU* SUFFER LIKE THAT ALL SUMMER, MR. WEATHERBEE?

GOLLY, NO!

I DIDN'T WASTE MY SUMMER STUCK IN THE HOUSE-- (HOUSES), LIKE THAT! I DID SOME *TRAVELING!!*

DO TELL!

3

A VERY EXCITING SUMMER! BELIEVE YOU ME!!

YOU SAW EXOTIC PLACES?

THE USUAL TURTLE RACING AT CORN COB CORNERS!

YOU *DIDN'T*?

LAND SAKES!

IT BOGGLES THE MIND!!

THE GIRL'S A TRUE ADVENTURESS!

THEN OFF TO MUDVILLE FOR THE TRACTOR COMPETITION!

ROAR

- A WEEKEND OF SHEEP SHEARING IN WALNUT GROVE!

THERE'S NO STOPPING THIS FOOTLOOSE FILLY!

THAT'S A **23-MILE** TREK!

A REGULAR CHARLES KURALT!

WANDERLUST! NO DOUBT ABOUT IT!

WAS THERE *MORE?*

4

THE SWEET POTATO PIE BAKE-OFF IN HAYSEED HOLLOW!

YOU ATTENDED *THAT?*

EGAD!

WELL, YOU CERTAINLY HAD AN EXHILARATING SUMMER, BETTY!

TOO BAD *YOU* WERE STUCK AT HOME THE WAY *YOU* WERE!

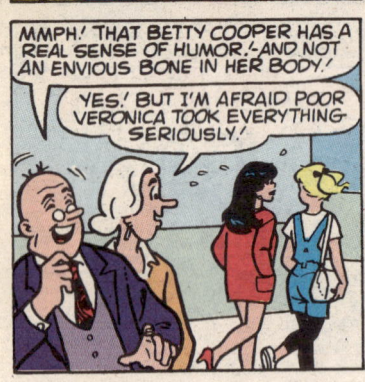

MMPH! THAT BETTY COOPER HAS A REAL SENSE OF HUMOR!-AND NOT AN ENVIOUS BONE IN HER BODY!

YES! BUT I'M AFRAID POOR VERONICA TOOK EVERYTHING SERIOUSLY!

NEXT SUMMER YOU WANT TO STAY HERE IN RIVERDALE WITH BETTY?

YES, DADDY! SHE DOESN'T GET BORED THE WAY I DO!

SHE TRAVELS AND SEES THINGS! SHEEP SHEARING, TRACTOR SHOWS, TURTLE RACES, PIE BAKE-OFFS!! IT ALL SOUNDS SO WONDERFUL!

?!

DON'T ASK *ME*, SIR! A BOGGLED MIND SEEMS TO *GO* WITH THE JOB!

The End

Betty -in- "DECISION MAKER"

Archie: WHAT DID YOU WANT TO SEE ME FOR, BETTY?

Betty: I WANT YOU TO MAKE A DECISION FOR ME, ARCHIE!

Betty: TELL ME WHICH DRESS YOU WOULD LIKE ME TO WEAR TO THE DANCE!

Betty: I WANT YOU TO BE PROUD OF ME SATURDAY NIGHT!

1

I LIKE THE ONE ON THE RIGHT, BETTY!

YOU DO? -- GEE, I KIND OF FAVORED THE ONE ON THE LEFT!

WELL THEN WHY ARE YOU ASKING ME?

BECAUSE I WANT TO PLEASE YOU!

SAY --- I KNOW HOW TO MAKE THE RIGHT DECISION!

?

COME ON, ARCHIE! DRIVE ME OVER TO RONNIE'S HOUSE!

WHAT FOR?

I'M GOING TO ASK HER WHICH DRESS I SHOULD WEAR TO THE DANCE!

2

IF I KNOW HER SHE'LL PICK OUT THE TACKY ONE FOR ME TO WEAR!

POP!

PING!

THEN I'LL JUST WEAR THE OTHER ONE!

SMART, HUH?

POP!

PING!

I CAN'T TELL WHICH ONE I LIKE WITHOUT YOU WEARING THEM!

HOW'S THIS ONE?

I CAN'T TELL UNLESS I SEE THEM BOTH TOGETHER!

HERE, ARCHIE! SLIP THIS ON AND STAND NEXT TO ME!

WHAT?

ARE YOU CRAZY?

BE A SPORT! YOU WANT ME TO LOOK GOOD, DON'T YOU?

3

Archie

•ARCHIE DIGEST #192 ON SALE
SEPTEMBER 3RD•

Betty & Veronica

•BETTY & VERONICA DIGEST #132
ON SALE AUGUST 27TH•
•BETTY & VERONICA DOUBLE
DIGEST # 109 ON SALE
SEPTEMBER 10TH•

Jughead

•JUGHEAD DOUBLE DIGEST #88
ON SALE AUGUST 27TH•

Archie & The Gang

•LAUGH DIGEST #178 ON SALE
SEPTEMBER 17TH•

Betty and Veronica in "JUMP START"

ISN'T IT A BIT EARLY FOR A SECOND CHILDHOOD, DEAR HEART? YOU HAVEN'T FINISHED THE *FIRST* ONE YET!

PANT! PANT!

W- WHAT? (GASP!) WHASSAT?

JUMPING ROPE? YOU'VE REGRESSED?

WHEW! F- FINE EXERCISE!

OF COURSE, IT'S A FINE EXERCISE! THAT'S NOT THE POINT!

THE POINT IS-- WHO WANTS TO EXERCISE!

1

WHERE IN THE WORLD HAVE YOU BEEN KEEPING YOURSELF, GIRL?

EVERYBODY WANTS TO EXERCISE!

IT'S THE *NEW WAVE!* IT'S *IN!* IN TODAY'S WORLD IT'S AN ABSOLUTE MUST!

WITHOUT IT THERE *IS* NO BODY BEAUTIFUL!

I DEFY ANYONE TO COME UP WITH A BODY MORE BEAUTIFUL THAN *THIS!*

I GET QUITE ENOUGH EXERCISE JUST ADORING THIS EXQUISITE FIGURE!

OH, PISH POSH!

WITHOUT EXERCISE YOU GET SOFT!

EXACTLY MY POINT! SOFT IS WHAT A WOMAN SHOULD BE!

DO YOU REALIZE THE DANGERS YOU'RE RISKING WITH THAT STUPID ROPE?

LIKE GOOD HEALTH?

2

OKAY! YOU KEEP DOING THIS SILLY STUFF!

EVERY DAY!

AND WHAT DOES IT GET YOU?

VIM, VIGOR AND VITALITY!

SWEAT! SWEAT IS WHAT IT GETS YOU! AND -- UGH -- WORSE!

WORSE? LAND SAKES, LUCY! WHAT DO YOU CONSIDER WORSE THAN -- UGH -- SWEAT?

OKAY! BE FUNNY IF YOU MUST! BUT I'LL TELL YOU WHAT'S WORSE!

MUSCLES, THAT'S WHAT!

MUSCLES ARE BAD?

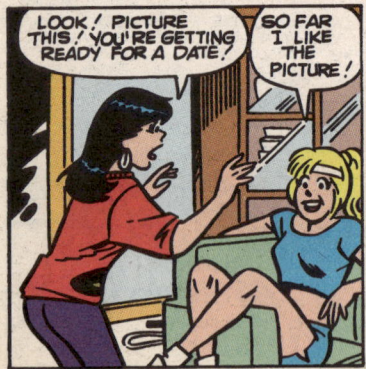

LOOK! PICTURE THIS! YOU'RE GETTING READY FOR A DATE!

SO FAR I LIKE THE PICTURE!

YOU'RE SHOWERED... ALL GUSSIED UP... PUTTING ON YOUR MAKE UP!

SLOW DOWN! I'M TRYING TO PICTURE GUSSIED UP!

3

HARK! THE DOORBELL!

I'M HARKING! I'M HARKING!

IT'S ARCHIE!

WELL, LET HIM IN!!

I'M ARCHIE! I GO--- "HI, DOLL!"

YOU'VE DYED YOUR HAIR, ARCH!

A LITTLE SWEET TALK....ROMANTIC TYPE CONVERSATION!

OH, PSHAW! I'LL BET YOU SAY THAT TO ALL THE GIRLS!

HE SLIPS HIS ARM AROUND YOU!

I BLUSH DELICATELY!

AACH!!

HE SCREAMS!! WHASSAT?

HUH? HUH? WHA...? WHA-?

HE RECOILS IN HORROR! YOU'RE NOT BETTY!

I'M NOT?

4

DON'T KID ME!! I FELT THAT *MUSCLE!*

WHO ARE YOU, REALLY? REGGIE? BIG MOOSE?

GREAT MAKE-UP JOB, FELLA, BUT YOU CAN'T FOOL OL' ARCH! ADIOS!

MMPH! YOU'RE FUNNY, RON! YOU'RE A REAL NUT!

DON'T SAY I DIDN'T WARN YOU FRIEND!

SOMETIMES MY BEST FRIEND IS A COMPLETE WHACKO!

SHE'LL GO TO ANY LENGTHS TO CONVINCE YOU SHE'S RIGHT ABOUT SOMETHING!

SO MUCH FOR THE "SWEAT"! NOW LET'S SEE WHAT'S GOING ON IN THE WORLD OUTSIDE!

5

"We've got a major problem! And I mean major!"

New title every month— 44 books available now!

TOPSY-TURVY

Sabrina's friends think her life is just peachy— great grades, amazing wardrobe—but they just don't get how hard it is to hide her witch status. So she casts a spell to put them in her shoes . . . and suddenly finds that her own powers have disappeared!

Available wherever paperback books are sold.

Based on the hit TV series

Sabrina The Teenage Witch

Topsy-Turvy

Sabrina's spell turns everything upside down!

Paul Ruditis

SIMON PULSE
www.SimonSays.com

Betty and Veronica in "ROYAL FLUSH"

GEE, MISS GRUNDY'S OUTDONE HERSELF THIS TIME!

YEAH! A HEAVY ESSAY ON ENGLISH ROYALTY -- DUE TOMORROW!

I BET JUGHEAD'S WILL BE ON *HENRY THE VIII*!

WELL, FORTUNATELY FOR ME, I WON'T HAVE ANY PROBLEMS WRITING IT!

THE LODGE FAMILY PROBABLY *ORIGINATED* THE ENGLISH ROYAL BLOODLINES!

TA, TA, PEASANTS!

1

THERE GOES A *TRUE* PATRIOT!

WHAT ARE YOU DOING YOUR REPORT ON?

I THINK I'D LIKE TO WRITE ABOUT *PRINCESS DIANA*--- MY MOM HAS SOME BOOKS ON HER!

MINE WILL BE ON QUEEN ELIZABETH I!

I'D BETTER GO GET STARTED ON IT!

ME, TOO! 'BYE, ARCHIE!

MUCH LATER...

BETTY, DEAR, IT'S *MIDNIGHT!*

I KNOW, MOM! BUT I'VE GOT TO GET THIS DONE!

TAC TAC TAC

WELL, I HOPE YOU KNOW WHAT YOU'RE DOING!

I WANT THIS TO BE A *GOOD* REPORT!

TAC TIC TAC TAC

WOW ... THEY HAD TO RESEARCH *DIANA'S BLOODLINE* PRETTY THOROUGHLY TO MAKE SURE SHE WAS *ROYAL* ENOUGH TO MARRY *PRINCE CHARLES!*

YAWN!

THE ROYAL COUPLE

2

STILL... HER LIFE WAS SO ROMANTIC.... IMAGINE MARRYING A *REAL* PRINCE.... JUST IMAGINE...

BETTY FALLS ASLEEP AND BEGINS TO DREAM...

WHAT ARE YOUR CHANCES OF MARRYING *PRINCE ARCHIBALD*, LADY BETTY?

WELL, I'VE BEEN VERY OPTIMISTIC...

POP!

...BUT THEN I HEARD THAT *LADY RONNIE* SOLD HER COUNTRY VILLA AND HAS MOVED INTO TOWN!

GREAT NEWS, YOUR LADYSHIP!

LADY RONNIE FELL OFF A CLIFF IN SWITZERLAND WHILE SKIING, RIGHT?

NO, NO! THE PRINCE HAS CHOSEN HIS BRIDE!

YOU'RE SUPPOSED TO FAINT *AFTER* I TELL YOU WHO IT IS, YOUR LADYSHIP!

SMILE, YOUR LADYSHIP!

SO WHO IS IT? WHO IS IT?? *TELL ME!!*

DON'T WRINKLE THE SUIT!

3

HE CHOSE YOU, BUT *DON'T* ASK ME WHY!

OH, I KNEW HE WOULD! HE HAS SUCH GOOD TASTE!

YOUR LADYSHIP, LADY RONNIE IS HERE FOR TEA!

HELLO, MY DEAR!

DON'T TAKE IT TOO HARD THAT PRINCE ARCHIBALD DIDN'T CHOOSE YOU, LADY RONNIE!

OH? WHY NOT?

WELL, I DON'T LIKE TO BOAST--BUT BLUE BLOOD REALLY SHOWS!

IS THAT SO?

I'VE AN IDEA YOUR ROYALTY IS AS PHONY AS YOUR HAT!

I BEG YOUR PARDON!

LET'S JUST SAY I'M HAVING A BLOOD TEST DONE! GOOD DAY, MY LADY!

WHAT A SORE LOSER!

4

5

THE ONE WHO RESEARCHED YOUR BLOODLINE - LADY RONNIE!

HELLO, MY RED-BLOODED FRIEND!

THIS CAN'T BE HAPPENING--- IT MUST BE A NIGHTMARE-- NIGHTMARE--

A NIGHTMARE--- OH! THAT'S ALL IT WAS! AM I GLAD IT WASN'T FOR REAL!

NEXT MORNING--

IF RONNIE'S BLOOD IS BLUE, IT'S PROBABLY AS DARK AS INK!

HEY, BETTY!

HI, ARCHIE! WHY AREN'T YOU WITH VERONICA?

OH, SHE'S AT HOME, MORTIFIED! SEEMS THERE ISN'T ANY MORE ROYALTY IN THE LODGE FAMILY TREE!

SHE FOUND OUT THAT ONE OF HER ROYAL ANCESTORS RAN OFF TO AMERICA WITH A SCULLERY MAID!

LIKE I SAID, SHE'S A TRUE PATRIOT!

END

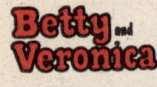

Betty and **Veronica**

in

"RAPID RECOVERY"

Archie "DIZZY TIZZY"

WHEEEEEE!

THE ROUGHER THE RIDE, THE BETTER I LIKE IT!

YAHOO!

SPACE SHUTTLE

GULP! SUDDENLY, I FEEL VERY DIZZY!

FROM THE RIDE?

XK E3

NO! FROM LOOKING INTO AN EMPTY WALLET!

$5.00 A RIDE

The END

Archie IN "ABOUT FACE"

ARCHIE, HOW WOULD YOU LIKE TO EARN TWENTY DOLLARS BY RUNNING AN ERRAND FOR ME?

I'D BE GLAD TO MR. LODGE--- WHEN AND WHERE?

I WANT YOU TO DELIVER SOME CONTRACTS TO A CLIENT OF MINE!

HE HAS TO HAVE THEM BY THREE O'CLOCK - HE HAS TO CATCH A PLANE!

I'LL BE RIGHT OVER!

THAT TWENTY BUCKS COULD GET ME BACK IN VERONICA'S GOOD GRACES!

SHE WAS REALLY MAD WHEN SHE GOT STUCK WITH THE BILL AT HAMBURGER HAVEN!

POW!

POP! PING!

I WAS SURE I HAD SOME MONEY ON ME, BUT I SPENT IT ALL THE DAY BEFORE!

COME ON IN, ARCHIE!

I'LL BE RIGHT WITH YOU, I'M JUST PUTTING THE FINISHING TOUCHES ON THE CONTRACTS!

WHAT ARE YOU DOING HERE?

2

4

NOW WHERE DID HE GO OFF TO AGAIN?

ARCHIE, GET BACK IN HERE, EVERYTHING IS READY!

LET ME GET YOU THE ADDRESS AND YOU'LL BE ON YOUR WAY!

YOU AGAIN!

SMITHERS! THROW HIM OUT AGAIN.!!

BUT LET ME EXPLAIN.!

OH THIS IS SUCH FUN.!

THUMP!

AND DON'T COME BACK.!!

SLAM!

I DON'T KNOW IF THIS KIND OF ABUSE IS WORTH A LOUSY TWENTY BUCKS!

END

YOUR ROUTINES ARE GREAT, VERONICA!

CHEERLEADING SQUAD TRYOUTS

ORDINARILY YOU WOULDN'T HAVE ANY TROUBLE MAKING OUR SQUAD, BUT—

BUT WHAT, SYLVIA?

CAPT.

THIS YEAR WE HAVE ONLY ONE OPENING, AND WE HAVE A CANDIDATE WHO'S IN A CLASS BY HERSELF!

WOW! BETTY HAS MORE MOVES THAN UNITED VAN LINES!

Betty IN

A GYMNASTIC TWIST

1

OH, ARCHIE! I MADE THE CHEERLEADING SQUAD!

IT LOOKS LIKE MY DREAM OF CHEERING YOU ON TO VICTORY IS FINALLY GOING TO COME TRUE!

HMPF! HER DREAM IS MY NIGHTMARE!

LATER..

NOT ONLY DOES THAT BLONDE BUBBLE-HEAD BEAT ME OUT OF THE CHEER-LEADING SQUAD...

---BUT SHE GETS THE INSIDE TRACK WITH ARCHIE!

WHAT ARE THE PROSPECTS FOR OUR GYMNASTIC TEAM, MISS GRUNDY?

TERRIBLE!

ALL THE MEMBERS OF MY CHAMPIONSHIP TEAM GRADUATED!

I HAVE NO ONE LEFT BUT INEXPERIENCED FRESHMEN!

2

HMM! THIS MAY BE MY CHANCE TO PRY GOLDILOCKS LOOSE FROM ARCHIE!

MISS GRUNDY, HAVE YOU SEEN BETTY PERFORM?

SHE'S A *BORN GYMNAST!* SHE DOES IT ALL— DIVE ROLLS, FRONT FLIPS, DOUBLE TWISTS---

SHE'S IN MY ENGLISH CLASS NEXT PERIOD! I THINK I'LL HAVE A TALK WITH HER!

BETTY, WHY HAVEN'T YOU COME OUT FOR GYMNASTICS?

'CAUSE I'D RATHER BE A CHEERLEADER, MISS GRUNDY!

I THINK YOU'D MAKE A BIGGER CONTRIBUTION TO THE SCHOOL AS A GYMNAST!

MISS GRUNDY IS *RIGHT!*

AS A CHEERLEADER YOU'RE MERELY CHEERING ON THE BOYS!

---AS A GYMNAST YOU'D SERVE AS A ROLE MODEL FOR ALL THE *GIRLS* OF RIVERDALE!

3

ARE YOU GOING TO LET YOUR SCHOOL DOWN?

GOSH! WHEN YOU PUT IT THAT WAY, I GUESS I HAVE NO CHOICE!

NOW I'LL HAVE ARCHIE WHERE HE BELONGS--- IN MY HIP POCKET--- THAT IS, IF I HAD A HIP POCKET!

THE NEXT DAY:

RONNIE, HAVE YOU HEARD THE BAD NEWS?

WHAT, SYLVIA?

BETTY RESIGNED FROM THE CHEERLEADING SQUAD!

OH, THAT'S *AWFUL!* I GUESS YOU'LL WANT ME TO TAKE HER PLACE!

YES, I GUESS SO!

D-UH, YOU THINK *YOU* HAVE BAD NEWS, SYLVIA!

?

MOOSE 15

--- OUR QUARTERBACK ARCHIE FRACTURED HIS TOE AND WILL BE OUT FOR THE YEAR!

OH, DEAR!

4

OH, ARCHIE! I JUST HEARD ABOUT YOUR INJURY!

YEAH! IT'S A BAD BREAK-- IN MORE WAYS THAN ONE!

BUT I CAN'T WASTE TIME ON SELF-PITY!

I FIGURED OUT A WAY TO STILL MAKE A CONTRIBUTION TO OUR SCHOOL!

HOW?

I HEARD THE GYMNASTIC TEAM NEEDS A SCOREKEEPER, SO I VOLUNTEERED!

INSTEAD OF YOU CHEERING ME ON, BETS, IT LOOKS LIKE I'LL BE CHEERING YOU ON!

OH, THAT'S FANTASTIC!

RONNIE, I'M SO GRATEFUL YOU TALKED ME INTO SWITCHING ACTIVITIES!

YOU'RE A REAL CUPID!

YEAH! --- A STUPID CUPID!

END

DEAR DIARY... THE ELECTION FOR QUEEN OF THE FALL FESTIVAL IS TODAY!

VOTE! YOUR CHOICE FOR QUEEN OF THE FALL FESTIVAL

EVERY GIRL AT RIVERDALE HIGH SCHOOL HOPES SHE HAS A CHANCE! EVEN I DO!

WHO WILL BE QUEEN OF THE FALL FESTIVAL VOTE!

HOWEVER, I THINK VERONICA HAS OVEREXAGGERATED HERS SOMEWHAT...!

...AND IN CONCLUSION, I WANT TO THANK ALL THE LITTLE PEOPLE WHO CAME TO THE OBVIOUS DECISION OF CHOOSING ME!

SEWING 101

Betty's Diary
"CAMPAIGN MANAGER"

1

VERY GOOD! CAN YOU RECITE THE GETTYSBURG ADDRESS, NEXT?

BETTY!

CLAP! CLAP!

I WAS JUST REHEARSING MY ACCEPTANCE SPEECH AS QUEEN OF THE FALL FESTIVAL!

HOW DO YOU KNOW YOU'LL WIN?

THERE ARE OVER FOUR HUNDRED GIRLS IN THIS SCHOOL!

WHY, IT'S ONLY LOGICAL! I AM DESCENDED FROM ROYALTY...

...EVEN THOUGH IT WASN'T ENGLISH ROYALTY LIKE I ONCE THOUGHT, I AM OF ROYALTY!

I ALWAYS SAID YOU WERE ROYAL...

A ROYAL PAIN!

SEWING 101

MOST PEOPLE ARE *AWARE* OF THAT, BETTY DEAR! I DON'T NEED TO MENTION IT!

SEWING

AFTER ALL, THERE'S NOTHING WORSE THAN SOMEONE WHO BRAGS ABOUT THEIR HUMILITY!

I COULDN'T AGREE MORE!

2

THE ONLY TROUBLE WAS, RON'S—ER— "MODESTY" WASN'T GETTING HER VOTES!

IF SHE ASKS ME TO CALL HER "YOUR HIGHNESS" ONE MORE TIME I'LL SCREAM!

WHO, "QUEEN" VERONICA?

SHE WON'T HEAR IT FROM ME!

ONLY ARCHIE SEEMED IMMUNE TO HER ARROGANCE!

HE'LL BE HER ONLY VOTE!

I'M NOT VOTING FOR HER!

I WAS, BUT I CHANGED MY MIND!

I DECIDED IT WAS MY DUTY TO WARN HER!

EVEN IF SHE IS AN EGOTISTICAL SNOB...

SHE'S STILL MY BEST FRIEND!

HEY, RON!

BETTER CUT THE CROWING! IT'S NOT HELPING YOUR CHANCES ANY!

ME "CROW," ...AS IN... BRAG??

DON'T BE RIDICULOUS! I'D HARDLY BE SO VULGAR AS TO DO THAT!

THEN STOP ANNOUNCING YOURSELF AS THE WINNER!

THE VOTE ISN'T IN YET!

MAYBE SO... BUT WE ALREADY KNOW THE OUTCOME... DON'T WE?

3

VOTE FOR RON?... C'MON, BETTY!

THAT VAIN STRUTTING PEACOCK!

LISTEN! SHE MAY HAVE THE BIGGEST MOUTH IN THREE STATES... BUT SHE REALLY WOULD FIT THE PART!

YEAH, SHE DOES HAVE THE MAKINGS OF A DICTATOR!

A TRUE TYRANT!

NO, NO, NO! SHE HAS GORGEOUS GOWNS, GOOD BREEDING AND CHARM SCHOOL CULTIVATION!

TOO BAD IT DIDN'T TAKE ROOT!

OH, SHE'S REAL CHARMING!

SHE TOLD ME SO HERSELF!

USUALLY, SHE DOES KNOW HOW TO HANDLE SOCIAL SITUATIONS!

YEAH! SHE'S A BORN SNOB!

IT FIGURES BETTY WOULD TRY TO CAMPAIGN FOR VERONICA LODGE!

SHE SURE IS LOYAL!

TOTALLY SELFLESS!

SO WHO SHOULD WE VOTE FOR?

I DUNNO... I REALLY HADN'T THOUGHT ABOUT IT UNTIL NOW!

4

LATER, AT ASSEMBLY... THE VOTES ARE IN, STUDENTS! HERE ARE THE RESULTS!

YOU'RE A CINCH TO WIN, VERONICA!

WAS THERE EVER ANY DOUBT?

WISH I WAS!

I'LL TRY TO ACT SURPRISED WHEN THEY ANNOUNCE MY NAME!

YOU *DO* THAT LITTLE THING!

OUR FALL FESTIVAL QUEEN IS BETTY COOPER!

YAY!

HUH?!

Betty Cooper 304
Veronica Lodge 96

I DIDN'T EVEN HAVE TO ACT SURPRISED, DEAR DIARY!

B-BUT-- WHY ME?

THE MOST LOYAL, UNSELFISH, SWEETEST GIRL IN THE WHOLE SCHOOL!

COME ON, BETTY!

THE NEXT UNEXPECTED SURPRISE WAS EVEN BETTER!

AND NOW... IF OUR QUEEN WILL CHOOSE HER ATTENDANT PRINCE FOR THE FESTIVAL!

THAT'S EASY, ARCHIE ANDREWS!

WHAT?!?

BUT I DON'T THINK VERONICA WAS TOO HAPPY WITH THE OUTCOME...!

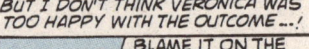

BLAME IT ON THE "LITTLE PEOPLE", RON! THE ONES YOU WERE COUNTING ON!

BAH!

THE "LITTLE PEOPLE" HAVE VERY LITTLE MINDS!

END

WHAT WILL I DO?

DON'T PANIC! WE CAN FIGURE OUT SOMETHING!

THERE ISN'T TIME ENOUGH TO BUILD A CYCLOTRON, OR AN OPERATING VOLCANO, OR EVEN A SIMPLE ROBOT...

I KNOW! HOW ABOUT AN ANT FARM?

TEE-HEE! IT SOUNDED LIKE YOU SAID "ANT FARM"!

I DID! IT'S FASCINATING! YOU CAN LOOK THROUGH THE GLASS AND SEE THE LITTLE DUDES HARD AT WORK!

YOU MEAN, WATCH ANTS?

IT SOUNDS GROSS!

NOT AT ALL! IT'D BE A SURE "A" IN SCIENCE!

WOULD I HAVE TO, LIKE, TOUCH THEM?

NO! ALL YOU'D DO IS OBSERVE THEM AND REPORT WHAT YOU SEE!

2

WHERE DO YOU GET ONE OF THESE CREEPY, CRAWLY CREATURE CONDOS?

JUGHEAD HAS ONE! I'LL BET HE'D LEND YOU HIS!

GEE, I DUNNO, ARCH! THIS IS KIND OF A CRITICAL TIME FOR MY ANTS! MARIANNE HAS GOT THE SNIFFLES...

...WALTER IS GOING THROUGH A MID-LIFE CRISIS AND MAY NEED PSYCHOLOGICAL COUNSELING, WANDA DOESN'T APPROVE OF HER DAUGHTER, CRYSTAL, MARRYING WARREN...

SO, I MAY GET A CHANCE TO SEE AN ANT ELOPE! GET IT? ANT-ELOPE! AND THEN, THERE'S LEON! I HAVE TO READ TO HIM EACH NIGHT OR HE WON'T GO TO SLEEP!

AND YOU THINK WALTER NEEDS PSYCHOLOGICAL COUNSELING?!

PLEASE, JUG, I PROMISE WE'LL BE VERY CAREFUL!

YOU CAN SET THAT THING DOWN OVER THERE!

CAREFUL, ARCH, SYLVESTER IS SUBJECT TO MOTION SICKNESS!

3

ARCH, I'VE GOT TEN ANTS!

YOU CHARGE THEM RENT?

NO, NOT TENANTS, *TEN ANTS!* TWENTY OF THEM ARE MISSING!

WHAT?

LOOK! THERE'S A CRACK IN THE SIDE! THAT MUST BE HOW THEY ESCAPED!

OH, NO! MOTHER'S GIVING A LUNCHEON FOR THE WOMEN'S CLUB TODAY!

WE CAN'T HAVE ANTS CRAWLING ALL OVER THE TABLE!

IT WOULD BE INTERESTING TO SEE HOW THEY ADAPT TO THIS NEW ENVIRONMENT!

WELL, YOU CAN SEE HOW THEY ADAPT TO AN EXTERMINATOR!

NO! NO! YOU *CAN'T!* THEY'RE MY FRIENDS!

JUG'S RIGHT! WE CAN'T KILL HIS ANTS! I HAVE AN IDEA! LET'S SET UP A PICNIC LUNCH OUTSIDE! ANTS LOVE PICNICS! THAT'LL ATTRACT THEM!

4

THIS HAD BETTER WORK! MY MOTHER'S GUESTS ARE ARRIVING!

LOOK! HERE COME THE ANTS!

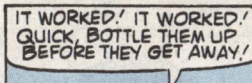

IT WORKED! IT WORKED! QUICK, BOTTLE THEM UP BEFORE THEY GET AWAY!

HEY! THESE AREN'T MY ANTS! THESE GUYS ARE STRANGERS!

WHAT?!

IF THESE AREN'T YOUR ANTS, THEN...

EEEEEEK!

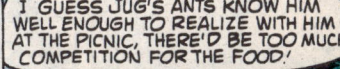

I GUESS JUG'S ANTS KNOW HIM WELL ENOUGH TO REALIZE WITH HIM AT THE PICNIC, THERE'D BE TOO MUCH COMPETITION FOR THE FOOD!

END

Betty in "A NEW TWIST"

THE RACE IS NOT ALWAYS TO THE SWIFT NOR THE BATTLE TO THE STRONG...

YES, YOU *CAN* WIN WHEN EVERYTHING'S GONE WRONG!

I'M GOING TO NEED YOUR SUPPORTING CHEERS AS I RUN IN THE WOMEN'S BIZZY FIZZ KOLA 10 K TODAY! ... HOW ABOUT IT?

LIKE TO, BUT...

SORRY!

BUSY!

CAN'T!

NO HELP THERE! ... I'LL CALL OL' RELIABLE RON... TEMPERAMENTAL AS SHE IS... *SHE* WON'T LET *ME* DOWN!

OY!

BETTY, DEAR, HAVE YOU FORGOTTEN?! I'M THROWING MY 6th SEASONAL SOCIETY PARTY OF THE YEAR *TODAY!*

NOW I RECALL... IN YOUR WORLD THERE ARE 8 SEASONS IN A YEAR!

1

YOU'LL HAVE TO TROT YOUR SCRAWNY LEGS OFF WITHOUT ME... BY THE WAY, MY SOCIETY PARTY IS GOING TO HAVE TV COVERAGE... WATCH FOR IT ON THE 6 O'CLOCK NEWS!

THANKS, RON! (SIGH)

I SUPPOSE YOU'VE CONNED MY ARCHIE INTO WATCHING YOUR SWEATY SCAMPER!

MY ARCHIE IS WORKING TODAY AT THE FETCH 'N' RETCH SUPERMARKET UP ON THRILL HILL...

...AND THE RACE ROUTE GOES RIGHT PAST FETCH 'N' RETCH WHERE MY ARCHIE HAS PROMISED TO BE WAITING FOR ME WITH A THIRST-QUENCHING DRINK OF CROC-ADE!

RUN ALL YOU WANT, BETTY, AS LONG AS IT ISN'T AFTER MY ARCHIE! CLICK!

RACE TIME...

BIZZY-FIZZ KOLA 10K

BEHIND THE STARTING LINE, GIRLS!

HMMPH! "MY ARCHIE," SHE SAYS!

BIZZY FIZZ KOLA

RUMBLE!

WEATHER LOOKS ABOUT AS ENCOURAGING AS MY FRIENDS!

READY, SET...

BLAM!

BIZZY FIZZ KOLA

2

2 MILES LATER...

THE LEAD PACK'S ALREADY AT THE TOP OF THRILL HILL AND THE REST ARE BEHIND ME... I'M KINDA BY MYSELF!

ARCHIE SHOULD BE UP THERE WITH MY CROC-ADE ...PUFF.! PUFF.! ...I'LL NEED IT AFTER THIS HILL.! PUFF.!

RUMBLE!

RATS! I WAS AFRAID OF THIS.!... RAIN!

LET'S GET INSIDE!

YAP! YAP!

BUZZ OFF, POOCHIE!

YAP! YAP!

3

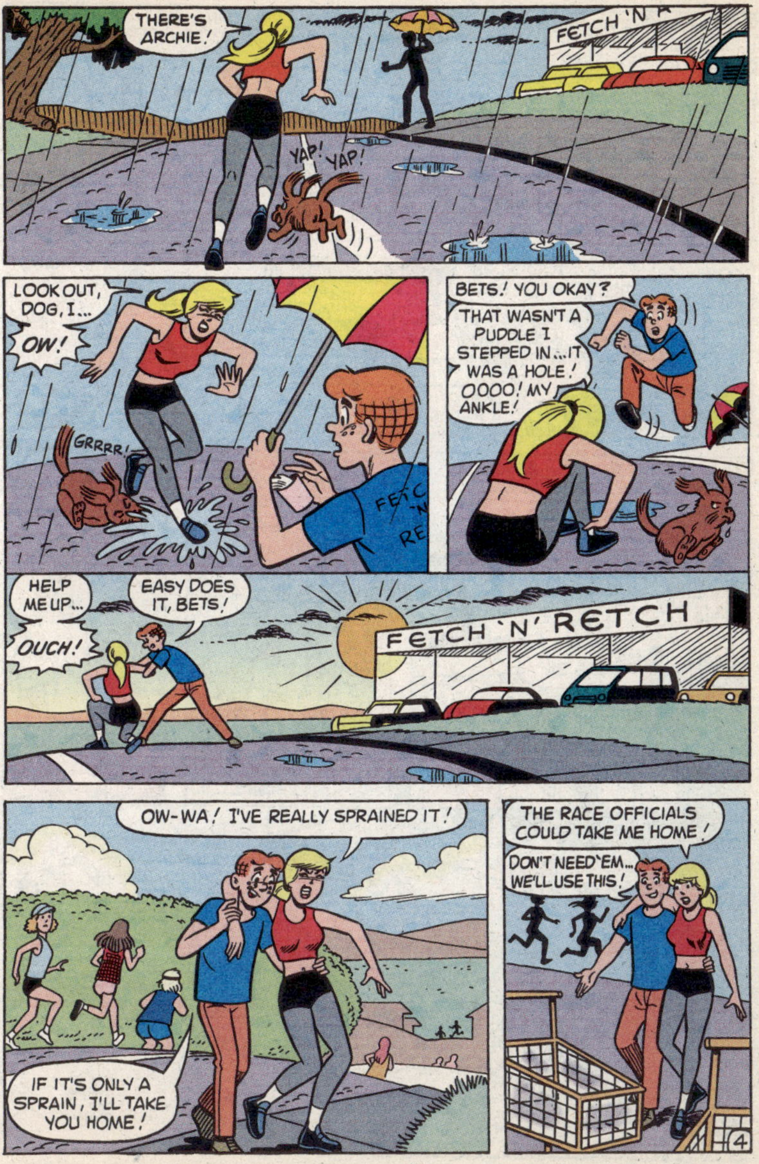

THERE'S ARCHIE!

FETCH 'N A[...]

YAP! YAP!

LOOK OUT, DOG, I...

OW!

GRRRR!

BETS! YOU OKAY?

THAT WASN'T A PUDDLE I STEPPED IN...IT WAS A HOLE! OOOO! MY ANKLE!

HELP ME UP...

OUCH!

EASY DOES IT, BETS!

FETCH 'N' RETCH

OW-WA! I'VE REALLY SPRAINED IT!

IF IT'S ONLY A SPRAIN, I'LL TAKE YOU HOME!

THE RACE OFFICIALS COULD TAKE ME HOME!

DON'T NEED 'EM... WE'LL USE THIS!

4

SOON... THANKS FOR THE BANDAGE, GUYS!... GLAD IT'S ONLY A SPRAIN!

COOPER

BETTY! WH... LET'S ALL SIT DOWN AND WATCH THE 6 O'CLOCK NEWS!

FETCH 'N' RETCH

MY BABY! MY DAUGHTER! MY HEROES!

FETCH

THAT NIGHT... IT WAS NICE OF YOU TO COME BACK, ARCHIE! I FEEL RESPONSIBLE FOR YOUR HAZARDOUS ADVENTURE, BETS, SO I'M GOING TO COME OVER EVERY NIGHT WITH A PIZZA AND WE'LL WATCH TV TOGETHER UNTIL YOUR SPRAINED ANKLE IS BETTER!

PIZZA

REALLY?!... WHEN THAT ANKLE'S BETTER, I JUST MIGHT TURN THE OTHER ONE!

THE END

NOW THAT'S AN OLD TWIST!

PIZZA

Veronica

"IN THE RIGHT"

END

MR. LODGE IN INDOOR-GAME

NOW THAT I'VE SET UP MY GOLF NET INSIDE, I CAN PRACTICE MY GOLF DRIVES RIGHT HERE IN MY EXERCISE ROOM!!

UH, OH! THERE'S A HOLE IN THE SCREEN!!

MAYBE I CAN GET A BLANKET TO THROW OVER THE HOLE!

1

IT'S NICE OUT HERE ON THE PORCH! LET'S WATCH SOME T.V.!

OKAY, BUT I THINK IT'S A LITTLE CHILLY!

UH, DO YOU WANT TO GO INSIDE?

NO, DADDY IS VERY UPSET BECAUSE HE COULDN'T GO GOLFING! I THINK IT'S BEST WE STAY OUT HERE!

I'LL KEEP YOU WARM!

I'M STILL CHILLY! GET ME A BLANKET, PLEASE!

RING

SMITHERS! GET THE PHONE! OH, WHERE IS HE? I'LL GET IT MYSELF!

HERE'S A BLANKET! I GUESS THEY LEFT IT HERE TO AIR IT OUT!

2

POK POK POK SMACK POK POK POK POK

SMITHERS!!

YES, SIR? DID YOU CALL?

DID YOU HEAR SOME-THING?

IT WAS PROBABLY THE T.V.!

④

THERE'S A REAL GOOD SHOW COMING ON NOW! IT'S ALL ABOUT THIS HORRIBLE MONSTER!

YAAGH!

WHAT A REALISTIC SCREAM!

OF COURSE IT IS! THAT'S DADDY!!

THIS TIME YOU REALLY DID IT, ARCHIE!

HONEST, SIR! I DIDN'T DO IT!... I REALLY DIDN'T DO IT!

THERE'S A HOLE IN MY GOLF SCREEN! DID YOU MOVE THE BLANKET THAT WAS COVERING IT?!

YES! AND IT'S A GOOD THING!

OTHERWISE YOU WOULDN'T HAVE NOTICED THERE WAS A HOLE!

THAT'S RIGHT!

END.

YOU DUDES BETTER BE SPORTING THE '70'S LOOK IF YOU EXPECT TO COME TO MY '70'S PARTY TOMORROW!

AS THEY USED TO SAY IN THE SEVENTIES, "BE THERE OR BE SQUARE!"

I SEE YOU KIDS ARE SPORTING THE FADS OF THE SEVENTIES!

DADDY IS INTO OLD-FASHIONED THINGS, TOO!

WALL STREET

ESPECIALLY WHEN IT COMES TO CURFEWS AND RULES ON DATING!

YOU BETTER BELIEVE IT!

DADDY, I'LL NEED SOME BUCKS TO DECORATE MY '70'S PARTY IN THE GOOD OLD-FASHIONED WAY!

SO DO IT IN THE GOOD OLD-FASHIONED WAY!

MAKE THE PARTY DECORATIONS *YOURSELVES!*

2

BETTY, WE'LL NEED PLENTY OF DYE IF WE'RE GOING TO DO THE TIE-DYEING DECORATIONS OURSELVES!

DID YOU SAY YOU WERE GOING TO DO TIE-DYEING?!

YES! I'LL GIVE OUR PARTY AN *AUTHENTIC* '70'S LOOK!

SEE, DADDY! WE HAVEN'T SPLATTERED TOO MUCH DYE ON OUR CARPET!

FORGET ABOUT DOING THE DECORATIONS YOURSELVES!

HERE'S THE MONEY FOR YOUR PARTY DECORATIONS!

AND THERE'S PLENTY MORE IF YOU RUN SHORT!

IT'S EASY WHEN YOU KNOW HOW!

3

PARTY NIGHT...

BACK IN THE '70'S WE FEMALES NEEDED PLATFORM SHOES TO RISE IN THE WORLD!

WE STILL DO!

I FOUND A LOT OF MY DAD'S OLD STUFF IN OUR ATTIC!

THOSE JEANS ARE A WORK OF ART!

ESPECIALLY WHEN BETTY IS WEARING THEM!

KEEP ON TRUCKIN

LOVE

PEACE

I HAVE A LOT OF OTHER DESIGNS I PLAN TO USE!

I HOPE NONE OF THOSE DESIGNS ARE ON MY ARCHIE!

DILTON SEEMS VERY EXCITED ABOUT SOMETHING!

④

HEY, GANG! I JUST DEVELOPED SOME MOOD T-SHIRTS!

"MOOD T-SHIRTS"? WHAT ARE MOOD T-SHIRTS?

STAR WARTS

BACK IN THE 70'S THEY HAD MOOD RINGS THAT CHANGED COLORS DEPENDING ON THE WEARER'S MOOD!

THESE SHIRTS TURN YELLOW IF YOU'RE HAPPY AND RED IF YOU'RE MAD!

MINE IS BEGINNING TO TURN YELLOW!

MINE, TOO!

LOOK! HERE COMES REGGIE WITH HIS DATE CHERYL BLOSSOM!

CHERYL!

HI, EVERYBODY!

ROCKi

WOW! MY MOOD T-SHIRTS REALLY DO WORK!

THE END

JEN FELLURE

DAVINA DAYZIE

Digest Fan Art
c/o Archie Comic Publ., Inc.
PO Box 419
Mamaroneck, NY 10543-0419

PREETIE
SANDHO

CALVIN
BELDMAN

FAN-90

Betty and Veronica in THERE IS THIS TRIANGLE!

EVERYBODY KNOWS THAT BETTY CHASES ARCHIE! (WHO DOESN'T KNOW THE TIME OF DAY!)

...WHO CHASES VERONICA... (WHO WON'T GIVE HIM THE TIME OF DAY!)

..WHO CHASES OFF BETTY... (WHO DOESN'T CARE WHAT TIME IT IS ... JUST AS LONG AS SHE CAN GET ARCHIE!)

1

GOT THAT? IF NOT, WE'LL SORT IT OUT FOR YOU ONE MORE TIME!

BETTY CHASES ARCHIE (OF THIS, THERE IS NO DOUBT!)

ARCHIE CHASES VERONICA... (IT MAKES BETTY POUT!)

ARCHIE DOESN'T ALWAYS GET VERONICA (NOT ENOUGH CLOUT!)

HOWEVER, VERONICA CAN'T STAND TO SEE BETTY GET ARCHIE! (IT MAKES VERONICA SHOUT!)

BUT...

2

HAVE YOU EVER WONDERED WHAT IT WOULD BE LIKE ANOTHER WAY?

SAY EVERYBODY'S ROLES WERE REVERSED OR SOMETHING?!...

WHAT IF VERONICA CHASED ARCHIE WHO CHASED BETTY WHO... WELL, YOU GET THE GENERAL IDEA...

CAST YOUR PEEPERS OVER THIS TERRIBLE SCENE...

ARCHIE! I'VE GOT TWO TICKETS TO SATURDAY'S ROCK CONCERT! WANT TO GO?

HMM?

BETTY! HEY, BETTY!

SNIFF!

3

WAAAH! JUGGIE! ALL MY MONEY AND ADVANTAGES, AND HE **STILL** CHASES THAT POOR LITTLE NOBODY!

LIFE IS TOUGH!

WHAT DOES HE SEE IN HER?

I DUNNO! HER BEAUTY, HER BRAINS, HER BLONDE HAIR... THE USUAL, I SUPPOSE!

YOU'RE NO HELP!

BETTY! I'VE BEEN LOOKING FOR YOU!

HMM?!

LET'S GO SEE THAT NEW MOVIE AT THE BIJOU!

DUTCH TREAT, I SUPPOSE?...

YEAH, I...EH... I'M KINDA SHORT THIS WEEK, AND I...UH...

FORGET IT!!

I'M NOT MADE OF MONEY, ARCHIE ANDREWS! EITHER YOU COME UP WITH THE MONEY OR DON'T EXPECT ME TO GO!

≥GULP!≤

4

RATS! *NOW* WHAT?! THERE'S NO TIME TO RAISE THE MONEY!

ARCHIE... WHAT ABOUT MY TWO TICKETS TO THE CONCERT?

HEY, THAT'S RIGHT, RON! YOU'RE A LIFE-SAVER! YOU'RE SO GENEROUS WITH YOUR WEALTH!

THANK YOU, ARCHIE!

IT'S BETTY'S FAVORITE ROCK GROUP, TOO! SHE AND I WILL HAVE A BLAST! NOW WE CAN KEEP OUR DATE!

BETTY?!

WAIT A MINUTE! WAIT JUST A DOGGONE MINUTE!

HUH?!

I'VE HAD ENOUGH OF THIS! WHO'S RESPONSIBLE FOR THIS *MAUDLIN SCENE*?

ER...OUR SCRIPT WRITER AND ARTIST!

SO! IT'S ALL *YOUR* FAULT! I SHOULD HAVE KNOWN! YOU WRITERS AND ARTISTS ARE ALL ALIKE! YOU'RE *NEVER* SATISFIED!

5

NOW SEE HERE! THERE'LL BE NO MORE FOOLING AROUND WITH SUCCESS! YOU PUT THINGS BACK THE WAY THEY BELONG! BESIDES, I'LL TELL THE EDITOR!

YOU THINK WE BETTER DO AS SHE SAYS?!

WHO ARE WE TO ARGUE WITH SUCCESS?

THAT'S MUCH BETTER!

RETURN TO THE STORY!

EVERYTHING SHOULD BE BACK TO NORMAL!

THANK YOU!

NOW, ARCHIE... ABOUT THE CONCERT!

HE WAS GOING TO TAKE ME!

NOT WITH MY TICKETS!

NOW, GIRLS...!

ARCHIE, YOU STAY OUT OF THIS!

SHEESH! IF THAT'S NORMAL...

...I'D HATE TO SEE WHAT'S ABNORMAL!

OH, JUGGIE-KINS! ♪

END·

Betty

THIS GIRL FOR HIRE

MOTHER, I'VE JUST GOT TO GET A WHOLE NEW WARDROBE! IT'S THE ONLY WAY I CAN COMPETE WITH VERONICA FOR ARCHIE'S ATTENTION!

THAT'S RIDICULOUS, BETTY! YOU HAVE A PERFECTLY ADEQUATE WARDROBE!

RIVERDAL

IF YOU WANT TO BUY MORE CLOTHES YOU'LL HAVE TO EARN THE MONEY YOURSELF!

BUT THESE DAYS THERE ARE NO JOBS FOR TEENS!

THEN MAKE YOUR OWN JOB! --- THINK OF SUPPLYING A SERVICE THAT DOESN'T EXIST!

IS THERE ANYTHING I CAN DO FOR YOU, MR. WALKER?

I WISH SOMEONE WOULD TAKE CARE OF THE VICIOUS DOGS ON MY ROUTE!

ODD JOBS WANTED BY BETTY COOPER 344-520

COOPER

IS IT WORTH $5.00 IF I DISTRACT THEM?

YOUNG LADY, YOU HAVE YOURSELF A JOB!

SHOO! SCAT!

THANKS, BETTY!

YOU MADE $5.00 FOR JUST A FEW MINUTES OF WORK?

BUT I ALSO LOST FIFTEEN DOLLARS, WHICH IS WHAT THESE JEANS COST ME!

BETTY, I SAW YOUR AD, AND I'VE GOT JUST THE JOB FOR YOU!

2

HELP ME IMPRESS THOSE CHICKS -- BY OOHING AND AHHING MY STUNTS! AND I ALSO WANT YOU TO ASK ME FOR MY AUTOGRAPH!

I'LL MAKE IT WORTH YOUR WHILE!

WOW! ISN'T HE *SUPER?*

WOULD YOU AUTOGRAPH THIS PLEASE?

MY PLEASURE!

THANKS, BETS! YOU REALLY HELPED ME IMPRESS THOSE FOXES!

ER, BUT WHAT ABOUT MY REWARD FOR THE JOB?

YOU GET TO KEEP MY AUTOGRAPH!

I SEE YOU HAVE ANOTHER ODD JOB!

YES, I'M PROVIDING JUG WITH SNACKS SO HE DOESN'T MISS HIS FAVORITE PROGRAMS!

JONES

SCRUMPTIOUS! INSTEAD OF YOUR FIVE DOLLAR FEE, I'M GIVING YOU SIX DOLLARS!

OH, WOW!

AND HERE'S MY I.O.U. FOR THAT AMOUNT! BURP!

I.O.U.?!

YES, YOU SEE I'M ER, SLIGHTLY OVERDRAWN ON MY ALLOWANCE!

LIKE ABOUT SIX MONTHS OVER-DRAWN!

SIGH! THIS TEN IS ALL I HAVE TO SHOW FOR MY WORK THIS WEEK! ---MOOSE PAID IT TO HELP HIM THINK UP ALIBIS FOR HIS BAD MARKS!

D-UH! SORRY, BETTY! I NEVER GOT TO USE YOUR ALIBIS! --- DAD WOULDN'T EVEN LET ME OPEN MY MOUTH!

4

Archie "IT'S YOUR MOVE"

WAH!

ARCHIE'S FAMILY IS MOVING OUT OF *TOWN*!

GOLLY! LIFE WON'T BE THE SAME WITHOUT OLD FRECKLE-SNOOT AROUND!

JUGGIE WILL MISS HIM THE MOST! HE WAS ARCHIE'S VERY BEST FRIEND!

SNIFF!

SO---I'LL JUST GET MYSELF *ANOTHER* BEST FRIEND!

1

JUGGIE! ..YOU'RE *CRUEL!*

LOOK!..WE'VE GOT EACH OTHER! ---*HE'LL* BE *ALONE!*

AS HIS BEST FRIEND, IT'S UP TO ME TO MAKE THE SACRIFICE!

WHAT SACRIFICE?

I'VE GOT TO MAKE HIM *GLAD* TO BE MOVING!

SILLY! HE'LL BE BROKEN HEARTED!

NOT IF HE HATES THE THOUGHT OF THIS TOWN!

---IF WE TURN HIM *AGAINST* US! IF WE MAKE HIM *DETEST* US!

YOU'RE RIGHT! I'VE SEEN IT DONE IN THE *MOVIES!*

≈SOB!≈ THE SUPREME SACRIFICE! ..OUR PARTING GIFT TO A BELOVED FRIEND!

2

RONNIE, BABY! HAVE YOU HEARD? MY DAD HAS BEEN TRANSFERRED TO ANOTHER TOWN!

WELL, THAT'S JUST DANDY! NOW WHO'S GOING TO TAKE ME TO THE DANCE NEXT WEEK?

IS *THAT* ALL IT MEANS TO YOU?

WHAT *SHOULD* IT MEAN?

AT LEAST IT'S THE *LAST* DATE YOU'LL BREAK WITH ME!

BOY! VERONICA DOESN'T EVEN CARE THAT I'M MOVING!

WELL, *I* CARE, PAL!

I DON'T WANT YOU SKIPPING TOWN UNTIL YOU PAY ME THE TWO BUCKS YOU OWE ME!

DON'T WORRY! YOU'LL GET IT, SHYLOCK! --- I THOUGHT OUR FRIENDSHIP MEANT MORE THAN A COUPLE OF BUCKS!

3

4

WELL, I'M SORRY TO DISAPPOINT YOU, SON, BUT MY TRANSFER WAS CANCELLED!

WE'RE NOT MOVING!

WHAT?

YOU MEAN I'M STUCK IN THIS CRUMBY TOWN WITH JUGHEAD AND THOSE OTHER CREEPS?

ARCHIE, BABY! WE JUST HEARD THE NEWS! YOU'RE NOT MOVING!

YIPPEE!

SMACK! SMACK!

WE CAN LIVE AGAIN!

?

I DON'T KNOW! THEY'RE NUTTY! ...BUT NICE!

YEA, ARCHIE!

The End

DEAR DIARY... WITH GREAT FONDNESS I STILL REMEMBER THE FIRST DOLLHOUSES DADDY BUILT FOR ME WHEN I WAS ONLY NINE YEARS OLD...

Betty's Diary
HOBBY LOBBY

...AND UP UNTIL TODAY, YOU COULD SAY THE WHOLE FAMILY WAS INTERESTED IN MY HOBBY OF MINIATURES...

...AND WHEN YOU FINISH THESE DOLLHOUSE CURTAINS, I'D LIKE SOME FURNITURE COVERS!!!

OH DEAR!

LATELY, LIFE SEEMS TO BE ONE NEVER-ENDING DOLLHOUSE PROJECT!

OH, MOTHER, YOU LOVE IT, AND YOU KNOW IT!

1

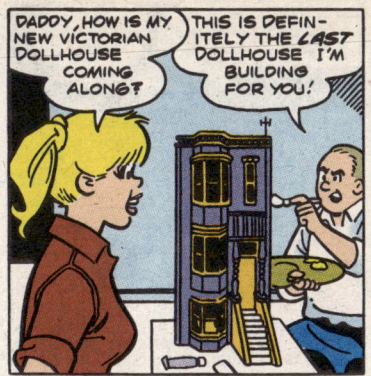

DADDY, HOW IS MY NEW VICTORIAN DOLLHOUSE COMING ALONG?

THIS IS DEFINITELY THE *LAST* DOLLHOUSE I'M BUILDING FOR YOU!

OH, DADDY! YOU LOVE BUILDING THEM!!

THEN WHY DO I KEEP IT SUCH A SECRET FROM MYSELF?!

BETTY, WE'VE DECIDED WE'D LIKE A WORD WITH YOU!

?

YOU OUGHT TO REAPPRAISE THIS DOLLHOUSE HOBBY OF YOURS!

WE THINK YOU'VE OUTGROWN IT!!

LATELY, WE'RE SPENDING MORE TIME ON *YOUR* HOBBY THAN *YOU* ARE!

ONLY BECAUSE I'M SO BUSY REPAIRING MY FRIENDS' CARS!

JUST LOOK AT THIS BASEMENT OF OURS! IT LOOKS MORE LIKE A DOLLHOUSE MUSEUM!

2

COME ON! WE'RE GOING OUT TO SPEND A DAY TOGETHER LIKE A *NORMAL* FAMILY! GET AWAY FROM ALL THESE DOLLHOUSE PROJECTS!

A FEW MINUTES LATER...

WHERE ARE WE GOING?!

...TO THE COUNTY FAIR!

WHEE! THIS IS FUN!

THIS IS THE KIND OF THING WE SHOULD HAVE BEEN DOING ALL ALONG!

CORN

DOG ON A STICK

YES, FROM NOW ON, I SEE A *BRAND NEW LIFESTYLE* FOR THE COOPER FAMILY!

SHOW

IF IT ISN'T THE COOPER FAMILY!

WHAT A COINCIDENCE! WE'VE JUST BEEN TALKING ABOUT YOU!

HOBBY

HOBBY SHOW

?

3

WE KNOW HOW YOUR FAMILY IS INTO DOLL-HOUSES!

WE'D LIKE ALL OF YOU TO JUDGE THE DOLLHOUSE COMPETITION IN OUR HOBBY SHOW!

325   326

NO! A THOUSAND TIMES "NO"!

?

UH, DADDY... DROP ME OFF AT ROD'S JUNKYARD! I HAVE TO PICK UP SOME SPARE AUTO PARTS!

FAIR EXIT

GEE! I'M BEGINNING TO SEE HOW MY DOLLHOUSE HOBBY HAS BEEN AN ORDEAL FOR THEM...

$200.00

ROD'S JUN

4

LATER...

GOOD NEWS, MOM AND DAD! I'VE DECIDED TO GIVE UP MY DOLLHOUSE HOBBY!

HALLELUJAH!

YOU'LL BE HAPPY TO KNOW I'VE SWITCHED TO A *NEW* HOBBY!

A *NEW* HOBBY?!!

A HOBBY THAT'S IN KEEPING WITH MY INTEREST IN CARS! FROM NOW ON, I'M GOING TO COLLECT *HUB CAPS!*

WHERE DO YOU WANT ME TO STACK 'EM, BETTY?

...AND MAYBE THE TWO OF YOU CAN HELP ME CLEAN AND POLISH THEM ALL!

YES, DEAR DIARY... I FORESEE THE DAY WHEN MOM AND DAD WILL BE JUST AS ENTHUSED ABOUT HUB CAPS AS THEY ONCE WERE ABOUT DOLLHOUSES...

END.

Betty and Veronica in "GOODBYE OL' PAINT.."

Veronica: BETTY, DARLING! WILL YOU BE SEEING ARCHIE TODAY?

Betty: VERONICA, DEAR, YOUR SPIES HAVE PROVIDED YOU WITH A FULL REPORT OF MY DATE WITH ARCHIE AND YOU *KNOW* IT!

Betty: HA, HA! WELL, ANYWAY WOULD YOU GIVE HIM THIS CAN OF PAINT I PROMISED TO SEND OVER? IT'LL SAVE ME A TRIP!

Veronica: *ANYTHING* THAT'LL SAVE YOU FROM GOING OVER THERE, *DARLING!!*

1

MOST UNUSUAL FOR HER TO GIVE UP THAT EASILY!

ER- WHAT'S THAT PIECE OF TAPE ON YOUR FINGER, VERONICA?

THIS TAPE, DADDY?

HEE, HEE! THIS WAS COVERING A LITTLE PINHOLE IN THE BOTTOM OF THAT PAINT CAN!

AND NOW THAT THE TAPE IS GONE, THE PAINT WILL DRIP ALL OVER BETTY'S OUTFIT!

TSK! WILL IT REALLY, DADDY DEAR?

EEYECH! WHAT A MESS!

ONE OF RONNIE'S LITTLE JESTS, I SUPPOSE!

(SIGH) YOU'RE A GOOD SUPPOSER, JUGGIE!

2

NO SENSE WASTING ANY MORE OF THAT GOOD PAINT! I'LL POUR WHAT'S LEFT INTO THIS PLASTIC CANDY BAG!

YOU'RE VERY ECONOMICAL, JUGGIE!

WASTE NOT, WANT NOT!

TELL ARCHIE OUR DATE IS OFF, WILL YOU? I'M GOING HOME TO CHANGE!

I'VE GOT AN IDEA OL' ARCH ALREADY *KNOWS* THE DATE IS OFF!

NOW HOW IN THE WORLD COULD HE?

PERHAPS HE'S BEEN INFORMED BY THAT LITTLE OL' HOLE PUNCHER, *VERONICA!*

(SIGH) YOU'VE BEEN THIS ROUTE BEFORE, OL' CHUM!

MANY TIMES!

3

NOW I WONDER WHY THE RICH AND NOTORIOUS RONNIE LODGE WOULD BE PARKED IN FRONT OF ARCHIE'S PAD?

OH! IS THIS ARCHIE'S HOUSE? I DIDN'T NOTICE!

YOU WOULDN'T KNOW THAT HIS DATE WITH BETTY IS OFF?

REALLY? WHY?

IT SEEMS THAT A CAN OF PAINT LEAKED ALL OVER HER DRESS!

HORRORS!

WHAT AN UNFORTUNATE ACCIDENT!

DO YOU ALWAYS GRIN LIKE THAT WHEN YOU HEAR TRAGIC NEWS?

I WAS MERELY THINKING HOW LUCKY IT IS I'M HERE TO HELP OUT MY DEAR FRIEND, BETTY!

4

WILL *YOU* TELL ARCHIE THAT HIS DATE WITH BETTY IS OFF?

I'D LOVE TO!

SOMEHOW I *THOUGHT* YOU WOULD!

OH! ONE OTHER THING!

YES, JUGGIE?

I SAVED WHAT PAINT THERE WAS LEFT! WOULD *YOU* LIKE TO GIVE IT TO HIM?

TSK! I GUESS THOSE CANDY BAGS JUST AREN'T STRONG ENOUGH TO HOLD *PAINT!*

5

Betty and **Veronica** in "TEAM THEME"

RONNIE, I'VE GOT GOOD AND BAD NEWS!

FIRST, THE *GOOD* NEWS!

OUR COACH HAS AGREED TO PUT A GIRL ON OUR VARSITY FOOTBALL TEAM!

WHAT'S THE BAD NEWS?

THE OPPOSING COACH HAS PUT ELEVEN GIRLS ON HIS TEAM!

END

HEY! HERE COMES RON IN HER SNAZZY LITTLE EGG-BEATER EIGHT!

HI, RON!

WOMBAT

OP'S

RON!

MAYBE I'M INVISIBLE AND DON'T KNOW IT!

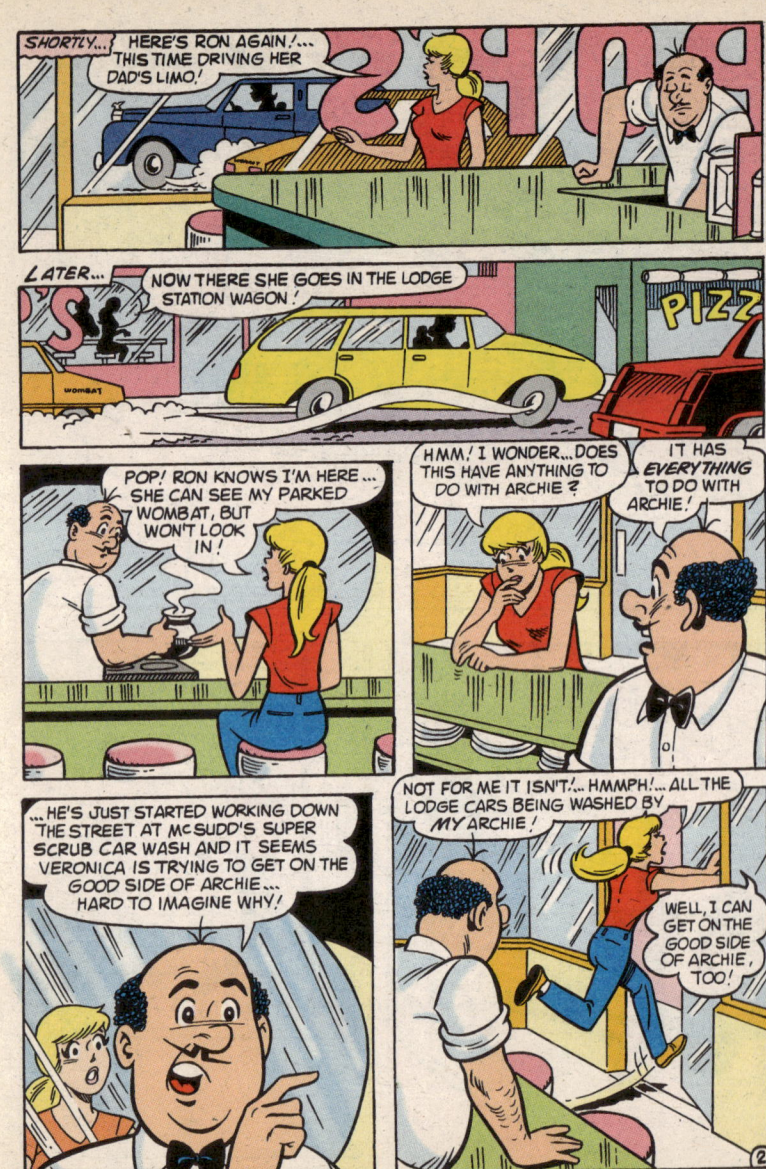

SHORTLY... HERE'S RON AGAIN!... THIS TIME DRIVING HER DAD'S LIMO!

LATER... NOW THERE SHE GOES IN THE LODGE STATION WAGON!

POP! RON KNOWS I'M HERE... SHE CAN SEE MY PARKED WOMBAT, BUT WON'T LOOK IN!

HMM! I WONDER...DOES THIS HAVE ANYTHING TO DO WITH ARCHIE?

IT HAS *EVERYTHING* TO DO WITH ARCHIE!

...HE'S JUST STARTED WORKING DOWN THE STREET AT MᶜSUDD'S SUPER SCRUB CAR WASH AND IT SEEMS VERONICA IS TRYING TO GET ON THE GOOD SIDE OF ARCHIE... HARD TO IMAGINE WHY!

NOT FOR ME IT ISN'T!... HMMMPH!... ALL THE LODGE CARS BEING WASHED BY *MY* ARCHIE!

WELL, I CAN GET ON THE GOOD SIDE OF ARCHIE, TOO!

2

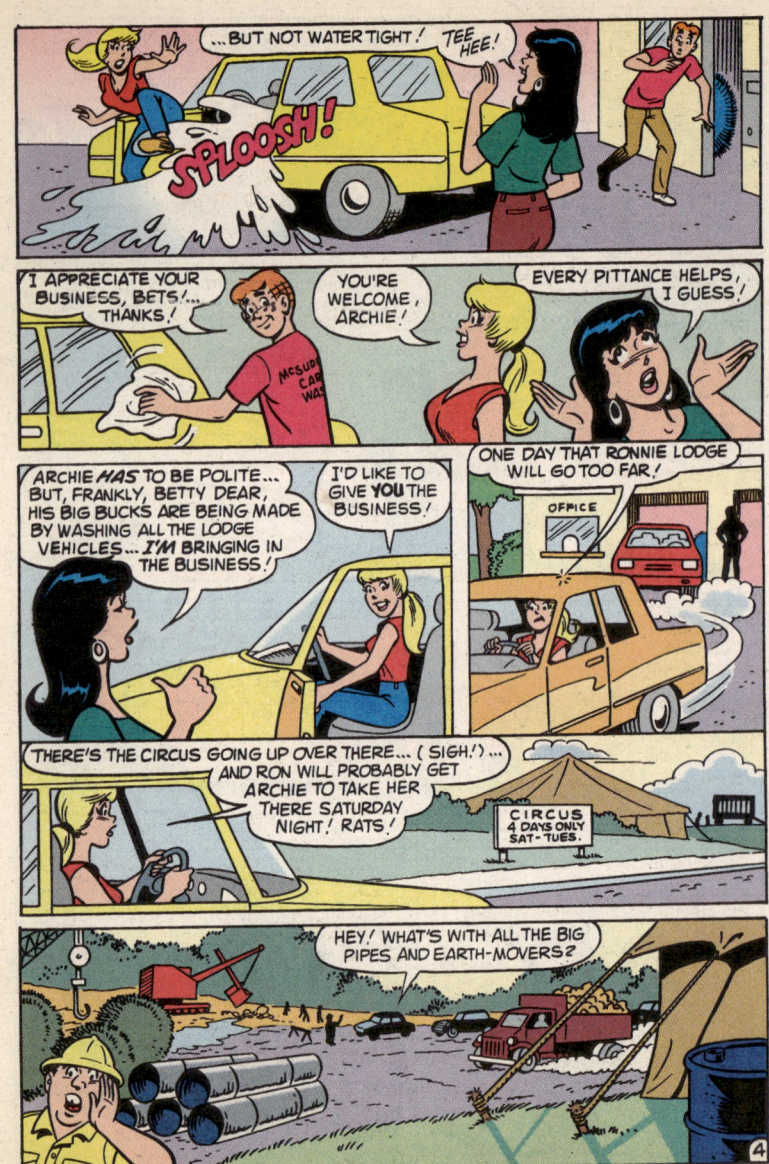

WHAT'S GOING ON, OFFICER O'LEARY?

WATER MAIN BREAK, BETTY... IT'LL TAKE 24 HOURS TO FIX IT!

WOMBAT

TOO BAD... THEY WERE JUST ABOUT TO WASH THE ELEPHANTS!

A MINUTE LATER...

MY! THAT'S A GRIMY HERD OF PACHYDERMS YOU HAVE THERE!

YES! THEY DO A LOT OF DIRTY CHORES AND WE HAVE NO WAY OF CLEANING THEM!

WOMBAT

SEC A ROW A

SEC B ROW B

I WOULDN'T SAY THAT!

WHAT DO YOU MEAN?

RING!

WHY, SURE!...NO,... I WON'T TELL ANYONE, MISS COOPER!

5

ASH

WATCH OUT, RON! DON'T GET YOUR DUNE-BUGGY SQUASHED!

!

RUB CAR WASH

EACH ELEPHANT IS THE SIZE OF 3 WOMBATS, SO I GUESS *I'VE* BROUGHT IN THE MOST BUSINESS!

IT WAS A PLEASURE WASHING YOUR ELEPHANTS EVEN THOUGH IT WAS A MAMMOTH JOB!

TEE HEE!

ARCHIE SEEMS A LITTLE TOO INTERESTED IN THAT CUTE LITTLE ELEPHANT TRAINER!

I'M GLAD WE AGREE ON SOMETHING, RON!

6

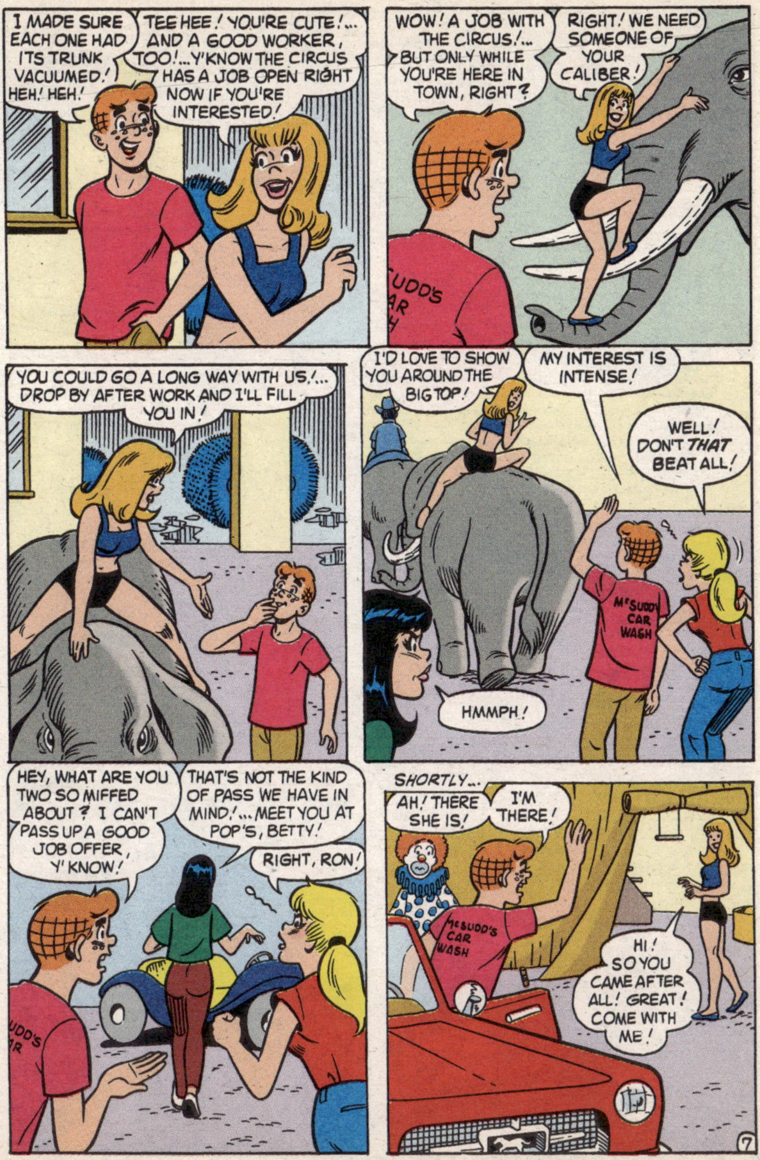

Panel 1:
I MADE SURE EACH ONE HAD ITS TRUNK VACUUMED! HEH! HEH!

TEE HEE! YOU'RE CUTE!...AND A GOOD WORKER, TOO!...Y'KNOW THE CIRCUS HAS A JOB OPEN RIGHT NOW IF YOU'RE INTERESTED!

Panel 2:
WOW! A JOB WITH THE CIRCUS!...BUT ONLY WHILE YOU'RE HERE IN TOWN, RIGHT?

RIGHT! WE NEED SOMEONE OF YOUR CALIBER!

Panel 3:
YOU COULD GO A LONG WAY WITH US!...DROP BY AFTER WORK AND I'LL FILL YOU IN!

Panel 4:
I'D LOVE TO SHOW YOU AROUND THE BIG TOP!

MY INTEREST IS INTENSE!

WELL! DON'T *THAT* BEAT ALL!

HMMPH!

Panel 5:
HEY, WHAT ARE YOU TWO SO MIFFED ABOUT? I CAN'T PASS UP A GOOD JOB OFFER, Y'KNOW!

THAT'S NOT THE KIND OF PASS WE HAVE IN MIND!...MEET YOU AT POP'S, BETTY!

RIGHT, RON!

Panel 6:
SHORTLY...

AH! THERE SHE IS!

I'M THERE!

HI! SO YOU CAME AFTER ALL! GREAT! COME WITH ME!

7

YOU SAID I'M THE RIGHT CALIBER AND I COULD GO A LONG WAY! ...GUESS I COULD BE A BIG SHOT, HUH?

YOU CERTAINLY WILL... RIGHT AFTER...

...YOU'RE SHOT OUT OF OUR CANNON!

ULP! YOU WANT ME TO BE A HUMAN CANNON BALL?

McSUDO'S CAR WASH

YOU'LL BE SHOT LOW... JUST TWO FEET OVER THE CROCODILE PIT TO LAND IN THAT NET... HOPEFULLY! IT'LL BE A CLASS ACT!

IT'LL BE MY LAST ACT!

McSUDO'S CAR WASH

MINUTES LATER...

HI, GIRLS, -ER- MIND IF I JOIN YOU?

SHALL WE LET HIM, RON?

OH, LET'S, BETS!

AND... SO I REFUSED THE CIRCUS JOB -ER- IT WAS OUT OF MY RANGE... AND -ER- I WAS AFRAID OF BEING FIRED! I HOPE YOU TWO CAN PARDON ME FOR BEING SO THOUGHTLESS TOWARD YOU!

HMMPH! ARCHIE, LIKE THE ELEPHANT, WE DON'T FORGET!...

...BUT WE DO FORGIVE!

SMACK!

SMACK!

THE END

VERONICA! TELL YOUR DAD I'LL BE OVER TONIGHT WITH THE PLANS FOR THE NEW BRIDGE!

SURE, ARCHIE!

?

Betty and Veronica

IN ONE TRACK MIND!

HMMPH!

WHY DOES YOUR FATHER HAVE ARCHIE WORKING ON COMPLICATED THINGS LIKE BRIDGE PLANS?

AND HE *HAS* BEEN AT YOUR HOUSE AN AWFUL LOT LATELY!

I GUESS YOU COULD SAY HE AND DADDY ARE DOING SOME *LAND DEVELOPING!*

①

LAND DEVELOPMENT?! GEE, I FIGURED HE'D HAVE TROUBLE WITH FILM DEVELOPMENT!

DADDY'S REALIZED ARCHIE IS TALENTED!

BESIDES, I THINK DADDY'S PLANNING FOR THE INEVITABLE FUTURE!

WHAT DO YOU MEAN?

YOU KNOW, ARCHIE AND I TOGETHER! THAT KIND OF THING!

I FIND THAT HARD TO BELIEVE!

OH, VERONICA! TELL YOUR FATHER I ALSO CAME UP WITH SOME LANDSCAPING IDEAS FOR THE MOUNTAIN!

OKAY, DEAR!

OOPS! GOTTA RUN! TOODLES BETS!

I JUST CAN'T BUY IT!

I THINK I'LL TAKE A CLOSER LOOK INTO THIS TONIGHT!

2

THAT NIGHT...

HI, VERONICA! WHERE'S YOUR DAD?

IN THE STUDY, ARCHIE!

GREAT! I CAN'T WAIT TO SHOW HIM THESE PLANS!

≷ SIGH ≷

♪ DING DONG... ♪

NOW WHO COULD THAT BE?

OKAY, WHERE IS HE?! I KNOW HE'S HERE! I WAS WATCHING OUTSIDE!

BETTY! THAT'S A GOOD LOOK FOR YOU!

DON'T GIVE ME THAT, "HE'S WORKING WITH DADDY" BIT! 'CAUSE I DON'T BUY IT!

TSK! TSK! JEALOUSY DOESN'T BECOME YOU, BETTY! THE GREEN CLASHES WITH YOUR HEAD-SCARF!

COME OVER HERE BY THE STUDY IF YOU WANT PROOF!

3

ARCHIE, WHAT DO YOU SUGGEST WE DO WITH THIS CLEARING HERE?

PUT IN A SHOPPING CENTER! IT IS CLOSE TO THE HIGHWAY!

WONDERFUL IDEA, MY BOY!

THANK YOU, SIR!

I DON'T BELIEVE IT! ARCHIE'S BECOMING A REGULAR POWER BROKER!

WHAT'D I TELL YOU! SOMEDAY SOON HE'LL BE READY TO TAKE HIS PLACE AS *MR. VERONICA LODGE!*

SNIFF! I JUST HOPE HE DOESN'T LOSE HIS SENSITIVE SIDE!

WELL, THOSE THINGS HAPPEN SOMETIMES!

BEFORE YOU KNOW IT HE'LL BE ONE OF THE WORLD'S TOP INDUSTRIALISTS!

ARCHIE, WHAT ABOUT THIS CHURCH?

YOU'RE GOING TO HAVE TO GET RID OF IT OR MOVE IT SOMEWHERE ELSE! IT'S IN THE WAY!

GAK!

4

WHAT'S HAPPENED TO HIM? THAT'S NOT THE SAME ARCHIE I'VE KNOWN!

UH, WELL...

ARCHIE ANDREWS! THAT DOES IT! HOW COULD YOU DECIMATE A CHURCH SO CASUALLY?

WELL, GEE, BETTY! IF IT'S THAT BIG A DEAL WE'LL JUST REROUTE OUR TRAIN TRACK!

TRACK LAYOUT "A"

A MODEL TRAIN LAYOUT?!

OH, DIDN'T I SAY THAT?

GIRLS! WHO CAN UNDERSTAND THEM?!

AMEN!

HEH! HEH!

TOOT! TOOT!

HELP!

THE END

Veronica IN "LIP SUNK"

HI, VERONICA! NICE DAY ISN'T IT?

POP'S

ARC-1

NO? IT'S NOT A NICE DAY? OH, YOU WANT TO PLAY CHARADES!

NECK? SOUNDS LIKE NECK? WRECK? DECK? NOT NECK? MOUTH? FACE? THE FACE IN THE BARROOM FLOOR? A FACE IN THE CROWD? MOUTH? LIPS? TEETH? TOOTH FAIRY?

NNRGNGNGH!

ROARRR! EEEEEK! BANG! BANG! DING!

CLICK CLICK

THERE ARE THE SOUNDS OF THE ROLLER COASTER AND THE SHOOTING GALLERY AND...ER...OH, YES... I HAVE TO FIND THE SONG!

...PASSED AWAY...

THERE IT IS!

I HAVE TO REWIND IT A BIT!

CLICK!

...DROPS ARE AWAITING THEE...

BEAUTIFUL DREAMER, WAKE UNTO TO ME...

THERE IT IS!

LATER:

...LED BY THE MOONLIGHT, HAVE ALL PASSED AWAY!

PERFECT! NOBODY WILL BE ANY THE WISER!

THE DAY OF THE RECITAL!

I'VE GOT THE TAPE ALL SET ON THE RIGHT SPOT! WHEN YOU'RE READY TO START, WAVE YOUR HANDKERCHIEF!

RIVERDALE HIGH SCHOOL

4

Betty

in

"Say it with Flowers"

THAT'S RIGHT, ARCHIE—TOMORROW'S MY BIRTHDAY! WHY DON'T YOU STOP BY? WE'LL HAVE A LITTLE PARTY JUST FOR THE TWO OF US!

ARCHIE DOESN'T KNOW IT YET, BUT AFTER TOMORROW HE'LL BE MINE, ALL MINE!

THE NEXT NIGHT—

HI, ARCHIE!

HAPPY BIRTHDAY, BETTY! ER... HERE ARE SOME FLOWERS!

I'LL JUST PUT THESE WITH THE REST OF THE FLOWERS I GOT!

HOLY COW! THIS PLACE LOOKS LIKE A FLORIST'S!

TO BETTY WITH LOVE — TED

LOVE GARY

George

THERE'S THE DOORBELL AGAIN! PROBABLY SOME MORE FLOWERS!

RING!

IT'S SO NICE OF BOB TO REMEMBER!

(GULP!)

1

THIS IS RIDICULOUS! I'VE BEEN ANSWERING THE BELL ALL DAY!

FORGIVE ME, ARCHIE!

ER...THAT'S ALL RIGHT, BETTY!

RING!

AREN'T THESE CARNATIONS FROM RICHARD SIMPLY ADORABLE?

MAYBE NOW WE'LL HAVE A MOMENT TO OURSELVES, ARCHIE!

HMM! I HAD NO IDEA BETTY WAS THIS **POPULAR**! MAYBE I SHOULD BE SEEING **MUCH MORE** OF HER!

THERE'S THAT DARN BELL AGAIN! WOULD YOU PLEASE ANSWER IT, ARCHIE! I'M SO TIRED OF GETTING UP!

SURE, BETTY!

RING!

WHO'S IT FROM THIS TIME, ARCHIE?

THE FLORIST! -HE WANTS TO KNOW WHEN YOU'RE GOING TO PAY HIM FOR ALL THE FLOWERS YOU ORDERED!

2

The End

MISS GRUNDY COULD MAKE A FORTUNE FROM THESE THINGS IF ONLY SHE'D LISTEN TO US!

WHAT A GREAT PARTY IT'D MAKE IF EVERYBODY CAME DRESSED UP IN THESE OUTFITS!

THAT'S IT! WE'LL GIVE A NOSTALGIA PARTY!

AND WE'LL SELL THESE COSTUMES AT THE PARTY!

BOYS! HELP US CART THESE CLOTHES AWAY!

HEY! DIG ME IN THIS 40'S FEDORA!

I THINK THEY USED TO CALL THIS THE *DRAPE SHAPE!*

DON'T ANYONE STEP ON MY BLUE SUEDE SHOES!

SNAP!

③

THE FOLLOWING WEEK—

HOW DID THE RUMMAGE SALE GO?

WE MANAGED TO RAISE $250!

IT'S NOT ENOUGH TO BUY ALL THE THINGS WE HOPED TO BUY-- BUT IT'S A START!

MISS GRUNDY! MR. WEATHERBEE!

YOU'VE GOT TO COME TO BETTY AND RONNIE'S NOSTALGIA PARTY AT THE LODGES'!

EVERYBODY IS WEARING THE CLOTHES YOU DISCARDED AT THE RUMMAGE SALE!

THIS I'VE GOT TO SEE!

WE SOLD OUT EVERYTHING!

WE EVEN BOUGHT OUTFITS THAT WE WORE WHEN WE WERE YOUNG!

④

RONNIE, THIS CHIC, VINTAGE CREATION IS WORTH EVERY PENNY OF THE THIRTY DOLLARS THAT I PAID!

COME ON IN AND SEE OUR PARTY!

I'M STUNNED! ABSOLUTELY STUNNED!

WE HAVE SOMETHING THAT WILL STUN YOU EVEN MORE, MISS GRUNDY!

HUH?

A CHECK FOR FIVE HUNDRED DOLLARS FOR THE SCHOOL LIBRARY!

IT'S WHAT WE MADE FROM ALL YOUR WORTHLESS DISCARDS!

END

Betty

IN

SPECIAL DISH

ARCHIE, I'M PREPARING A NEW DISH IN HOME ECONOMICS AND I'M GOING TO NAME IT AFTER YOU!

GREAT! WHAT IS IT?

A SIDE OF MEAT AND A HEAD OF LETTUCE!

THAT'S AN ODD COMBINATION!

AREN'T YOU EXCITED?

YES, BUT I DON'T UNDERSTAND!

HOW DO I ENTER THE PICTURE?

IT'S CALLED "MEATHEAD!"

WELL, DON'T GET MAD! EVERYONE ELSE KNEW IT WAS NAMED FOR YOU!

END

Betty and Veronica in "FRAME GAME"

PUT YOUR ARM AROUND ME, ARCHIE, AND HELP ME SUPPORT THIS HEAVY BALL!

YOU BET, BETTY!

DIG BETTY! PLAYING THE "HELPLESS FEMALE"! WELL-- TWO CAN PLAY THE GAME!

3

4

HI, ARCHIE!

OH, HI, RONNIE!

THIS LOOKS INTERESTING! COULD YOU HELP ME BOWL, TOO?

AS SOON AS I FINISH HELPING BETTY!

1

ARCHIE! WHY DO THE BALLS HAVE THESE FUNNY-LOOKING HOLES?

HOLY COW! YOU ARE A BEGINNER!

5

I THINK RONNIE NEEDS HELP MORE THAN YOU, BETTY!

I'D LIKE TO HELP HER ALL RIGHT! --- RIGHT OUT OF TOWN!

HOLD THE BALL THIS WAY AND FACE THE PINS!

"PINS"? WHAT ARE PINS?

LOOK, ARCHIE! I DID WHAT YOU TOLD ME! I THREW A STRAIGHT BALL!

IT CAN'T GO ANY STRAIGHTER THAN THAT! AREN'T YOU PROUD OF ME?

--ER--NOT EXACTLY!

2

3

THIS TROPHY FOR BOWLING A "200" GAME LAST WEEK!

ULP!

SO! YOU OUTRAGEOUS PHONEY! AND ALL THE TIME YOU PRETENDED YOU COULDN'T BOWL!

AND I HAVE SOMETHING FOR YOU TOO, MISS LODGE!

HUH?

THIS SUPER GOLD TROPHY FOR CAPTURING THE WOMEN'S SINGLES THE OTHER NIGHT!

HMPH!

I SEE IT NOW! BOTH OF YOU PRETENDED YOU COULDN'T BOWL SO YOU COULD GET YOUR JOLLIES AT MY EXPENSE!

WELL-- I DON'T DIG PEOPLE PLAYING ME FOR A FOOL!

4

GO FIND YOURSELF ANOTHER MEDIOCRE BOWLER TO MAKE FUN OF!

ARCHIE! COME BACK!

WE WEREN'T PLAYING YOU FOR A FOOL!

VERDALE BOWLING

WE DID IT SO WE COULD SPEND MORE TIME WITH YOU!

REALLY?

YES!

ISN'T THERE SOME WAY WE COULD MAKE IT UP TO YOU?

COME TO THINK OF IT-- THERE IS!

LET'S GO BACK! YOU CAN BOTH TEACH ME HOW TO BOWL!

END 5

I NEVER SEEM TO HAVE A MINUTE TO MYSELF! I'M ALWAYS ON THE GO!

BUT YOUR LIFE SEEMS SO EXCITING TO ME!

I'D GIVE ANYTHING TO HAVE THE PEACE AND QUIET YOU HAVE ... JUST LISTENING TO YOUR MUSIC, RELAXING AT HOME!

OH, RONNIE! THE GRASS ALWAYS SEEMS GREENER ON THE OTHER SIDE!

BUT THE GRASS REALLY IS GREENER ON YOUR SIDE!

Betty and Veronica IN THE WISH!

I WISH WE COULD WAKE UP TOMORROW AND YOU COULD BE ME AND I COULD BE YOU ... AND THEN WE'D *BOTH* BE HAPPY!

WISHING FOUNTAIN

1

YAWN! WHAT IS A PHONE DOING IN MY ROOM?!

RING!

OMIGOSH! I'M IN VERONICA'S ROOM!

DID OUR WISH REALLY COME TRUE... OR AM I JUST DREAMING?!

RRINGG!

YES... OH, HI, ARCHIE!

I'D LOVE TO MEET YOU AT POP TATE'S... WHEN?... IN AN HOUR? FINE! I'LL BE THERE!

WITH VERONICA'S WARDROBE, I'LL REALLY BE ABLE TO IMPRESS ARCHIE!

GOOD GRIEF! HOW DOES SHE EVER CHOOSE WHAT TO WEAR?!

...AND THERE'S ONE CLOSET AFTER ANOTHER!

GOOD MORNING, BETTY! HERE'S YOUR BREAKFAST!

FIFI IS TREATING ME LIKE I BELONG HERE!

2

I'M MEETING ARCHIE TODAY, FIFI! DO YOU THINK I SHOULD WEAR THIS OUTFIT?

YOU HAVE NO TIME FOR ARCHIE TODAY, MY DEAR!

...AND MRS. LODGE IS TREATING ME LIKE I WAS HER DAUGHTER!

MISS HOPKINS IS HERE TO FIT YOU FOR YOUR NEW CLOTHES!

NEW CLOTHES?! WHY DO I NEED NEW CLOTHES?!

AFTER THE FITTING I'VE MADE APPOINTMENTS FOR A FACIAL, A MANICURE AND A HAIRDO!

YOU HAVE A BUSY SCHEDULE AHEAD OF YOU!

AS SOON AS WE FINISH DISTRIBUTING THESE BOOKS WE HAVE TO GO TO MY CLUB FOR A SPECIAL LUNCHEON!

MRS. LODGE...UH, I MEAN "MOTHER," WHEN AM I GOING TO HAVE SOME TIME FOR MYSELF?

NOT TODAY, BETTY, YOUR FATHER INVITED THE CALDWELLS OVER FOR DINNER!

NO WONDER RONNIE SAID SHE'D GIVE ANYTHING JUST TO BE ABLE TO MOPE AROUND!

3

THE WISH REALLY *DID* COME TRUE! I'M IN BETTY'S HOME!

HOW LUCKY BETTY IS TO HAVE ONLY A FEW THINGS TO PUT ON!

NO FIFI! NO ENDLESS ROUNDS OF SOCIAL DUTIES!

WHY DID YOU PUT ON YOUR GOOD DRESS, VERONICA?

GO RIGHT UP AND PUT ON YOUR OLD JEANS! YOU KNOW YOU'RE HELPING ME WITH THE HOUSE CLEANING!

OH, THIS IS LOVELY! JUST THE TWO OF US!!

OF COURSE THERE'S JUST THE TWO OF US! WHO ELSE IS GOING TO HELP US WITH ALL THESE CHORES?

HOURS LATER...

WHEW! I'VE NEVER WORKED SO HARD IN MY LIFE!

THAT'S ENOUGH OF A REST! WE STILL HAVE TO TAKE DOWN THE CURTAINS AND WASH THE WINDOWS!

OH, GOOD! HERE COMES ARCHIE!

I DON'T BELIEVE IT! BETTY STOOD ME UP!

4

HI, ARCHIE!

HI, RONNIE! IS MY ALGEBRA HOMEWORK READY?

NO, ARCHIE! I HAVEN'T HAD A CHANCE!

WELL, MAYBE WE'LL DROP BY LATER... IF YOU PROMISE TO BAKE SOME CHOCOLATE CHIP COOKIES!

I CAN'T BELIEVE IT! HE'S TREATING ME THE WAY HE TREATS BETTY!

HURRY, VERONICA! WE STILL HAVE THE GARAGE TO DO!

THAT NIGHT...

YES, I KNOW, RONNIE... UNFORTUNATELY!!

BETTY, MY STUPID WISH CAME TRUE!

TUNA

MAYBE WE'LL WAKE UP AND REALIZE IT WAS ALL A BAD DREAM!

WELL, I'M NOT TAKING ANY CHANCES!

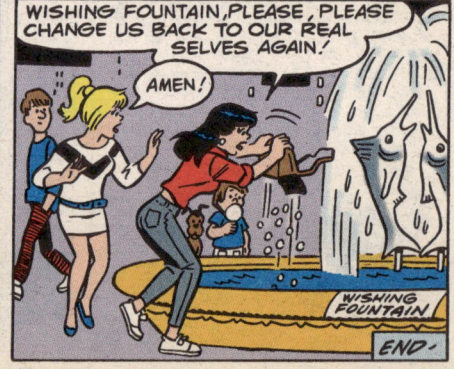

WISHING FOUNTAIN, PLEASE, PLEASE CHANGE US BACK TO OUR REAL SELVES AGAIN!

AMEN!

WISHING FOUNTAIN

END.

Betty's Diary "LEND ME YOUR ERA"

1

"AND GETTING A LOT OF DUMB SUGGESTIONS..."

OH, I CAN TELL YOU ALL ABOUT THE FIFTIES!

"IT WAS A PRIMITIVE TIME WHEN FOLKS WORE ANIMAL SKINS AND COMMUTED TO WORK BY DINOSAUR TRANSIT...

8:03 LOCAL
ALL STOPS TO QUARRY TOWN

AND ROCK CONCERTS WERE GIVEN BY MUSICIANS WHO PLAYED REAL ROCKS!

VERY FUNNY, JUGGIE!

BUT I CAN SEE IF I WANT TO FIND OUT ABOUT THE FIFTIES, I SHOULD ASK SOMEONE WHO HAS LIVED IT, LIKE MY PARENTS!

GEE, BETTY, IN THE FIFTIES, WE WERE YOUNGER THAN YOU ARE NOW!

EVERYTHING SEEMED SO MUCH BIGGER THEN!

... ALTHOUGH THAT COULD BE BECAUSE WE WERE SMALLER THEN!

2

I HAVE AN IDEA! WHY NOT GO DOWN TO THE VIDEO STORE AND RENT SOME MOVIES FROM THE ERA?

THAT'S A GREAT IDEA, DAD! I'LL REALLY BE ABLE TO GET A FEEL FOR THE TIMES THAT WAY!

LATER: LET'S TRY THIS MUSICAL "ROCK AROUND THE DOCK" FIRST!

CLICK!

SON, I LIKE THE WAY YOU PLAY THAT GUITAR! HOW MUCH DO YOU MAKE DRIVIN' A TRUCK?

$18.00 A WEEK, SIR!

HOW WOULD YOU LIKE TO MAKE $75.00 A WEEK PLAYING MUSIC?

ACME TALENT

COL. PACKER

$75 A WEEK?!! WOW!! YES, SIR!

DID PEOPLE ACTUALLY MAKE SO LITTLE MONEY THEN?

3

YES, BUT DON'T FORGET, THEN NEWSPAPERS COST 5¢ AND BUS FARE WAS A DIME AND PIZZA, 15¢!

ARE THOSE FOLKS GOING TO A COSTUME PARTY?

NO, THEY REALLY DRESSED LIKE THAT THEN!

LET'S TRY THIS SCIENCE FICTION MOVIE "JOURNEY TO THE WEST SIDE OF VENUS"!

CLICK

WHIRRRRRRRR

GEE, WHAT A FUNNY-LOOKING SPACESHIP!

AT THAT TIME, THE FIRST MOON LANDING WAS A DECADE AWAY...

...AND WE HADN'T LEARNED MUCH ABOUT OTHER PLANETS YET!

LIKE THAT THE SURFACE TEMPERATURE OF VENUS IS 900°!

LOOK AT THAT OLD COMPUTER! IT TAKES UP A WHOLE ROOM!

YES! AND NOW THAT THING COULD FIT INTO YOUR POCKET!

4

Betty in "Person to Person"

I'D LIKE A DOZEN RED ROSES FOR A VERY SPECIAL PERSON!

THAT'LL BE $30, YOUNG MAN!

FLOWER MO...

ISN'T THAT A RATHER EXPENSIVE GIFT FOR A HIGH SCHOOL STUDENT TO BE BUYING?

SEND FLOWERS

YEAH! I'VE HAD TO SAVE UP FOR AWHILE! BUT BELIEVE ME, SHE'S WORTH IT!

1

FLOWER WORLD

SEN FLOW

I TOLD BETTY TO MEET ME AT THE PARK!

WAIT'LL SHE SEES THESE-- SHE'LL FLIP!

HI, BETS!

HI, ARCHIE! WH-WHAT'S IN THAT BOX?

OH, ARCHIE! FLOWERS!! FOR ME?! OH! OH!! OH!!

SMOOCH!

D-UHH!

I CAN'T WAIT TO SHOW ETHEL AND VERONICA AND MOM AND DAD...

2

THEN, I'LL PRESS EACH AND EVERY ONE AND PUT THEM IN MY MEMORY BOOK! THEN I'LL—

SNIFF

OH,— MOOSE! WHAT'S WRONG?

AWW— ME AN' MIDGE HADDA FIGHT AN' NOW SHE WON'T TALK TO ME!

IF ONLY I COULD THINK OF SOME WAY TO MAKE UP WIT' HER!

HMMM..

HERE, MOOSE! GIVE HER A ROSE! THAT SHOULD DO THE TRICK!

HEY! THANKS, BETTY! THAT'S A SWELL IDEA!

HE'S HAPPY, AND I STILL HAVE ELEVEN LEFT FOR ME!

MOOSE

HI, LYDIA!

OH, HELLO, BETTY—

3

WHAT'S THE MATTER? ARE YOU OKAY?

JUST FEELING A LITTLE BLUE TODAY, DEAR-- I'LL BE ALL RIGHT!

WELL, HERE'S SOMETHING TO PERK YOU UP!

THANK YOU, BETTY! THAT'S VERY SWEET OF YOU!

I FEEL BETTER ALREADY!

AND SO-

OH! BIG ETHEL'S SICK? THEN GIVE HER THIS ROSE!

HOW NICE! THANK YOU!

FORGOT YOUR MOM'S BIRTHDAY? OH DEAR-- BETTER GIVE HER A ROSE!

THANKS, BETTY!

LOST YOUR WEDDING BOUTONNIERE? WELL, YOU CAN USE THIS ROSE!

GEE, THANKS, MISS!

I'M SORRY-- I DON'T HAVE ANY MONEY! BUT HERE'S A ROSE!

YOU'RE A SAINT, LASSIE!

GIVE

UNTIL FINALLY--

OMIGOSH! I ONLY HAVE ONE LEFT!

4

OH, MOTHER! I CAN'T BELIEVE WHAT I'VE DONE! ARCHIE BOUGHT ME A DOZEN ROSES AND I HANDED THEM ALL AWAY-- ONE BY ONE!

HOW WILL I *EVER* EXPLAIN THIS TO HIM?

HERE HE COMES NOW, DEAR!

HI, BETTY! I WANTED TO SHOW JUG THE ROSES I BOUGHT FOR YOU!

I GAVE THEM AWAY!!

OH, ARCHIE! I'M SORRY! I KNOW YOU MUST HAVE SPENT A FORTUNE ON THEM, BUT I KEPT RUNNING INTO PEOPLE WHO SEEMED TO NEED THEM, AND--AND--

CAN YOU EVER FORGIVE ME? SAY SOMETHING!

AW, BETTY! IT'S OKAY! THAT'S WHY I GAVE THEM TO YOU IN THE FIRST PLACE!

'CAUSE YOU'RE SUCH A *SPECIAL* PERSON!

END

EDITOR'S NOTEBOOK

Dear Archie Readers,

Be on the lookout for ARCHIE AMERICANA SERIES: BEST OF THE FORTIES - BOOK 2. By popular demand we are pleased to present another collection of stories from the frantic forties. In the forties when comics had an "anything goes" quality, Archie was there with all his wacky antics and hilarious tales. In the tradition of the Archie Americana Series, this is a high quality 96-page trade paperback. Definitely a collector's item to be enjoyed by the entire family. This book will be available on or about September 18.

Featured in ARCHIE & FRIENDS #62 is a story entitled "A Change of Plans." Mr. Lodge invites the kids to accompany him to rustic old Silverton, an authentic "Old West" town. His plan is to convert this town into an amusement park. They soon find out the town has its own version of fun and adventure.

In JUGHEAD #147 Reggie won't cut Jughead any slack, but is willing to cut Jughead's slacks. However, Reggie's cutting prank backfires when Jug is turned into a trend setter. Also in this issue, Trula Twyst returns and Jughead meets the challenge of the day as he tries to find a Halloween costume that will conceal him from her. Don't miss it.... on sale next month.

A monster sighting sends the gang investigating Lodge Manor, a creepy castle that was once the Lodge family ancestral home. Mr. Lodge had it shipped to the U.S. stone by stone, brick by brick. No one lives there except for a strange caretaker. There's more than monsters behind "The Mystery of Lodge Manor." You'll go bananas when you pick up your copy of ARCHIE'S WEIRD MYSTERIES #24.

A new family moves into a luxurious home next door to Veronica. Our credit card princess, who has been watching too many mobster movies lately, thinks her new neighbors are gangsters. Veronica sets up surveillance and comes up with some startling evidence. But what does she do next? Read "Ron Takes a Hit" in VERONICA #132.

Send your letters to: Victor Gorelick, Editor
Archie Comic Publications, Inc.
P.O. Box 419, Mamaroneck, NY 10543-0419.

1210D

Betty & Veronica in *Game Face Off!*

EASY, RON. CAREFUL! NO! NOT *THAT* WAY! QUICK! STEER YOUR Z-WING FIGHTER TOWARD THAT PLANET. HURRY!

YES, YES...

WHIRR!

ZOWIE!

ZOOM!

Pellowski
DeCarlo
Smith

WHAP! WHAP! ZAP!

YES! VICTORY!

UH-OH!

KA-BLOOEY!

TA-DA! ONCE AGAIN, COMMANDER MANTLE IS THE ULTIMATE V-CUBE-BOX CHAMPION!

HIP! HIP!

HOORAY!

WHO? WHO? WHO IS THE CHAMPION? I AM! I AM! I AM THE CHAMPION!

OKAY! OKAY! TRY NOT TO BE SO MODEST ABOUT IT, WILL YA?

GEE, SORRY, LADIES. BUT WHAT ELSE CAN I SAY? *I AM THE CHAMPION!* NO ONE CAN BEAT ME!

YOU CAN'T, BETTY! YOU CAN'T, RON. ARCHIE CAN'T, JUG CAN'T.

NOW I'M ALMOST SORRY I BOUGHT THIS NEW GAME SYSTEM.

WHY, RON? V-CUBEBOX IS THE ULTIMATE HOME GAMING SYSTEM.

TRUE. BUT SINCE REGGIE STARTED COMING OVER HERE TO PLAY, HE'S BECOME THE ULTIMATE PAIN IN THE NECK!

YOU COULD JUST *NOT* INVITE REGGIE OVER.

NO, THAT WOULD BE ADMITTING DEFEAT. WE'VE GOT TO FIND SOMEONE WHO COULD BEAT HIM AT THIS GAME.

2

THANKS FOR HAVING ME OVER, RON. I'VE GOTTA' GO NOW, BYE, BYE!

COME BACK ANY TIME... CHAMP!

IF WE USE OUR BRAINS, I'M SURE WE'LL COME UP WITH A WAY TO SILENCE REGGIE!

BRAINS! THAT'S IT! THE BEST PERSON TO PLAY A COMPUTER GAME IS A GENIUS.

The Next Weekend...

HERE I AM, EAGER TO SHOW OFF MY TALENT AGAIN, RON. THANKS FOR GIVING ME A CHANCE TO SHINE!

HUMPH! DON'T WORRY, REG. *THIS* WILL BE *MY* PLEASURE!

IN FACT, I HAVE A NEW OPPONENT WAITING FOR YOU.

REALLY? WHO IS IT?

HI, REG! READY TO GET BUSY?

HIM?! DILTON DOILEY? FINE! BRING IT ON, BRAINIAC BOY!

3

SORRY, RON. I COULDN'T OUTPLAY OR OUTWIT HIM. REGGIE IS TOO GOOD.

THERE MUST BE SOME WAY TO DEFLATE HIS EGO...!

HEY! I'M RICH! I CAN HIRE THE FOLKS WHO DESIGNED THE GAME TO TEACH REG A LESSON!

THAT WOULDN'T QUIET REGGIE. HE'D CLAIM THEY HAD AN UNFAIR ADVANTAGE AND HE'D BE RIGHT.

THEN I'LL JUST SCRAP THE SYSTEM. I CAN'T TAKE ANYMORE OF REGGIE'S BOASTING.

WAIT! I JUST THOUGHT OF SOMEONE WHO CAN GIVE REG A RUN FOR HIS MONEY.

OF COURSE! I SHOULD HAVE THOUGHT OF HIM SOONER! HE'S THE PERFECT CHOICE. I'LL BRING HIM HERE TOMORROW.

OKAY, I'LL MAKE SURE REGGIE IS HERE!

THE FOLLOWING AFTERNOON:

HA! HA! GREETINGS... LOSERS. WHO DID YOU ARRANGE FOR ME TO PLAY TODAY? ONE OF DILTON'S ROBOTS?

VERY FUNNY! ACTUALLY, CHAMP, WE HAVE SOMEONE WITH A REPUTATION EQUAL TO YOURS. SO, STEP RIGHT IN AND LET THE GAMES BEGIN!

5

THE CONTEST STARTS...

GULP! I HAVE TO ADMIT, THIS GUY IS GOOD!

I THINK REG HAS *FINALLY* MET HIS MATCH!

NO! *NOOO!* GET YOUR FIGHTER AWAY FROM MY SPACE STATION!

TAP! TAP!

YEOW! HE DESTROYED MY *ENTIRE* SPACE FLEET!

ZAP! ZAP!

KA-BOOM!

NICE WORK, MARTY! I'M GLAD DILTON BROUGHT YOU OVER.

SO AM I. THIS SYSTEM IS COOL! I DON'T GET TO PLAY IT VERY OFTEN.

MARTY IS THE REIGNING VIDEO CHAMP OF MY NEIGHBORHOOD!

MARTY, YOU'RE WELCOME TO PLAY MY SYSTEM WHEN-EVER YOU WANT TO.

GEE THANKS, RON!

I'M NOT SURE WHICH IS WORSE, LISTENING TO REG BOAST OR LISTENING TO HIM WHINE.

BEATEN BY A 10-YEAR OLD! HOW HUMILIATING!

END

6